'But you don't love me!'

Roxanne broke from Stanwyck's embrace.

'Blast it, I love you!' He punctuated this declaration by taking her in his arms and kissing her wildly on the face and mouth. For one dizzying moment, Roxanne feared she might swoon, but that would never do in the midst of anything so enjoyable. Reluctantly, she broke the embrace again.

'In all conscience, I must acquaint you with a change in my circumstances. I may have little dowry to bring to our marriage. If you wish to rethink the matter, I shall understand.'

'The only thing I wish to rethink,' he said, 'is whether to kiss you on the lips or the cheek.'

Clarice Peters was born in Honolulu, Hawaii, where she still lives with her husband, Adrian, a high school principal and her son, Jeremy. She's worked as an advertising copywriter, freelance curriculum writer and substitute teacher. She enjoys golf and tennis and has a weakness for Italian food.

Roxanne is Clarice Peters' third Masquerade Historical Romance, her other titles are *Thea* and *The False Betrothal*.

ROXANNE

Clarice Peters

MILLS & BOON LIMITED
ETON HOUSE   18-24 PARADISE ROAD
RICHMOND   SURREY   TW9 1SR

First published in Great Britain 1989
by Mills & Boon Limited

© Laureen Kwock 1989

Australian copyright 1989
Philippine copyright 1989
This edition 1989

ISBN 0 263 76466 4

Set in Times Roman 10¼ on 12 pt.
04-8906-66971 C

Made and printed in Great Britain

CHAPTER ONE

ON THE third occasion of his sister Gwendolyn's complaint that she was hungry enough to eat a bear, his lordship the Marquis of Stanwyck bowed to the inevitable. Gwen, it appeared, must eat!

'I did warn you that the journey would be long and that you had best eat a hearty breakfast,' he reminded her as he called up to Albert, his groom, to pull in at the next inn they encountered. 'And you'—he pulled his head back into the travelling-chaise—'dismissed that as mere prattle.'

'Well, I assumed we would stop for luncheon,' Lady Haverly protested, sending a supplicating look at the languorous figure sprawled across from her. As always, she felt a mild pang of vexation that Nigel should have inherited that striking combination of blue eyes and curly jet-black hair, while she was saddled with the more ordinary combination of blue eyes and straight yellow hair. Despite the best intentions of scores of hairdressers, her golden hair never did hold a curl.

'You can't expect me to starve,' she said now, returning to the point at hand. 'Particularly when I was so obliging as to accompany you to Aunt Gertrude's for the se'nnight, and even though we lasted only two nights with her, I dare say she was as happy to see the last of us as we were of her.'

'Probably happier,' the Marquis replied, examining a speck of lint that he had pulled off the shoulder of his coat of Bath-blue superfine. 'And why do we visit her once a year, Gwen? I vow, she hates it every bit as much as we do!'

'It is a family tradition,' Lady Haverly declared authoritatively, 'and, as such, beyond mere logic.' She brightened. 'But at least we shan't have to see her now for a whole year. And it is fortunate that Constance told me she was holding her festival at Brumley. We are in no hurry to return to London and can enjoy our time with her. She will have musicians and singers and acting troupes!'

'Will there be gypsies, too?' the Marquis asked.

'I don't know.' Lady Haverly paused for a moment's thought before recognising too late the twinkle in her brother's eyes. 'Oh, you odious creature, you are roasting me! I shan't listen to your excuses. You owe it to me to accompany me to the festival.'

'I am always at your disposal, Gwen,' Stanwyck said with the greatest civility.

'No, you're not! There was that time I was mad to see your Mrs Kinney at Drury Lane, and you practically ate me when I suggested we go there together.'

'The proprieties must be observed, Gwen,' he said, accepting with aplomb this passing reference to his latest *chère amie*. 'And she may not be *my* Mrs Kinney for long.'

His sister stared at him. 'Don't tell me she will be getting her *congé* so soon?'

He shrugged. 'After a time, my dear sister, all women become tedious in their demands.'

Lady Haverly eyed the lean figure across from her, wondering about the truth in this latest statement. Nigel at thirty-two was a confirmed bachelor—but she had often speculated privately to her Thaddeus that had Nigel not been so horribly jilted by that Crosby creature when he was little more than a greenhorn he might be happily married by now with a nursery filled with doting children, instead of flitting aimlessly from one *chère amie* to another.

'Perhaps you ought not to associate so much with women and spend more time with ladies,' she said.

Stanwyck's blue eyes widened with amusement, and a smile lifted the corners of his mouth, softening its sterner features. 'I ain't that thick in the muslin company!' he protested.

'That depends entirely on your point of view,' Lady Haverly replied, grasping his arm as the carriage dipped into a hole in the road. 'Before you took Mrs Kinney under your wing there was that opera dancer, and before her the ballerina on whom you squandered a ruby necklace, not to mention that flaxen-haired creature with the habit of taking snuff. How you could abide her I shall never know!'

The Marquis looked astonished at these reminiscences. 'I had half forgotten the ballerina myself,' he confessed. 'You are prodigiously well versed on my affairs. Keeping watch?'

'I am merely keeping myself abreast of what happens about me,' Gwen said with some dignity. 'I've never pinched or scolded you about your life, have I?'

Nigel was obliged to admit that she had not. That was the good thing about his sister Gwen, he thought with real affection. Much as she might deplore his habits of gaming and his fatal addiction to sport—not to mention his muslin dealings—she was not the sort to ring a peal over him.

'You are a good sister,' he said, trying for a humble tone.

His sister was not deceived. 'Don't use that tone with me, brother dear. And just what did Aunt Gertrude say to set you off? I vow you were as cross as crabs!'

The amusement drained from the Marquis's face, to be replaced by a look of distaste. 'She said I needed a wife.'

Lady Haverly paused. 'Well, now, Nigel, she might be right.'

The Marquis chortled. 'Your pangs of hunger have unhinged you, dear sister. I'd best fetch you a physician rather than a cook.'

'I wish you will be serious,' Gwen implored him. 'What, pray, is so unusual about taking a wife? You can't wish the title to die with you, can you?'

'What cheerful topics you raise, Gwendolyn. First a wife, and now my impending demise. I'll tell you as I told Aunt Gertrude, I have no intention of marrying. Jonathon' —he referred to his distant cousin and heir— 'can inherit it all.'

Lady Haverly shuddered. 'Jonathon is a block!'

The Marquis, being of a truthful disposition, did not dispute this statement. 'Yes, but that is a relief. He's so blockish he won't be plotting schemes against me.'

'And he's so addicted to travel,' Gwen went on. 'Albania, of all places, last year. Where is he now?'

'India, I believe. Or is it the Indies?'

'Well, there you see!' Gwen said emphatically.

Further speculation on the whereabouts of the Marquis's heir came to an abrupt halt as Albert pulled in at a posting-house. Lady Haverly, perceiving that she would be shortly sitting down to an ample luncheon, left the carriage to repair the damage that travel had done to her person.

The Marquis, trailing behind, was led into a private parlour by the landlord, who was rendered more than a little nervous at the sight of such Quality in his humble abode. After placing a tankard of the inn's finest ale in Stanwyck's hand, he left to rouse his wife to prepare the luncheon just ordered.

Stanwyck, sitting in a most uncomfortable chair, stirred restlessly as he reviewed the bumblebroth that had arisen with his aunt. By nature he avoided quarrels. They were too exhausting. Lady Gertrude Elcot was seventy if she was a day, and a griffin, but he had lost his temper when she had flung Drusilla Crosby in his face unexpectedly.

'You can't be still wearing the willow for that Crosby chit,' she had remarked with the bluntness for which she was famed.

Stanwyck, who had been walking her about the Shakespeare gardens, looked at her with a lifted brow. 'I fail to see why that should concern you, Aunt,' he replied in a voice that had been known to make grown men quake.

His aunt was not so affected. She stamped her cane on the stepping-stones as she walked. 'I just don't like to see you acting like a cake.'

'A cake?' Stanwyck's voice rose a fraction of an octave.

'Yes, a cake, and gudgeon, too, if you want the word with no bark in it. Find yourself another, that's what you would do if you had any brains. The kingdom's filled with agreeable-looking girls; marriage-minded ones too, I'd wager.'

'I am no recluse, Aunt! I have met some of those females.' And, he did not add, comparing any of them to the beautiful Drusilla was akin to comparing a monkey to Helen of Troy.

'You're not a monk, either, the way I hear of things,' his aunt grunted. 'Marriage is the ticket, Nigel.'

'I assure you, Aunt, that while I appreciate your concern, I go on very well at present.'

'No, you don't,' she contradicted. 'Anyone with half an eye can see you're devilishly unhappy.'

The Marquis lost his temper. 'I am not unhappy,' he retorted. 'And I shan't get married just to please you.'

'Hmph.' She snorted again. 'Well, I think...'

'Thank you, Aunt Gertrude, but I believe I can do my thinking for myself. I have done so since my majority, and now I recollect a letter I must write.'

Now, as he sipped his ale, Stanwyck felt that he had behaved badly. He should have been more tolerant of his aunt's foibles and would pen her a pretty apology as soon as he reached London. He also recalled a tea she favoured, a Chinese blend that was difficult and expensive to procure, and he made a note to order his secretary to have five pounds delivered to her with his compliments.

Having satisfactorily settled the quarrel in his own mind, he picked up the tankard in front of him, thankfully filled with something other than tea, and brought it up to his lips. As he did so, an ear-piercing scream shattered the calm of the inn. Half the ale spluttered back into the tankard.

'What the devil!' Stanwyck dabbed at his damp shirt with his free hand. The scream occurred again. He rose swiftly, crossed to the door, and stepped into the hall.

'You can't mean to leave me here, Orlando,' a female pleaded from the coffee-room. 'First to seduce and now to abandon me. Heartless, *heartless* man!'

'You're a queer one, missie,' a man said. 'And I shan't stay here a moment longer.'

With that a small, bearded figure bolted out of the coffee-room, nearly colliding with Stanwyck, who had been shamelessly eavesdropping.

The Marquis took a step back from the other man. 'I was sitting in the parlour and thought I heard a scream.'

'That was me!' a triumphant voice exclaimed. A girl, no more than sixteen, popped her head out of the coffee-room. And a pretty little head it was with raven hair, large blue eyes and a dimpled chin.

'I screamed,' she went on, looking rather proud of that fact. 'Wasn't it splendid?'

'It?' the Marquis asked, observing that while she had the look of Quality and her pink muslin frock was perfectly clean, it was not à la mode.

'My screaming,' the girl explained. He could have sworn that her eyes were dancing with glee. 'They used to tell me at Miss Thompson's School that my screaming could curdle the blood. I can sing and dance and do voices, too.'

The Marquis felt himself to be on uncertain ground. She did not look like a dimwit. 'Can you, indeed,' he murmured. 'A splendid accomplishment, I'm sure.'

'Here now, missie, you're confusing the gentleman,' the other man said.

'But, Orlando!'

'And stop calling me that.' He dealt an imploring look at Stanwyck. 'Females!'

'You might be gentler with your young love,' Stanwyck said, wondering about the relationship between the two.

The man recoiled as though struck. 'What did you say?'

'You see, Orlando! He thinks you've seduced me,' the girl said excitedly. 'Isn't it famous!'

'Oh, do lower your voice, missie,' the man pleaded. 'Land me in the suds, you will! God's truth, I've never laid eyes on you before a half-hour ago, and' —he drew himself up with dignity to his height of five feet and two inches—'I have *not* seduced you.'

'Yes, I know,' she said dismissively, 'but look how easily I convinced this gentleman that you had. And I didn't even rehearse! Think how much better I shall be with costumes and make-up and an audience!'

'Excuse me,' Stanwyck interposed, a glimmer of light starting to break through the fog. 'Are you saying you weren't seduced or in fear of your life?'

'Heavens, no, but it was good of you to think that! I had to convince Signor Fernando here that I was good enough for his troupe or he wouldn't let me go to London with him.'

Stanwyck turned to the other man. 'You, I take it, sir, are an actor?'

'I am the director of the Italian Players, my lord,' the man said, making a lavish bow and taking a card from his case. 'I merely stopped here for a bite to eat, and what must happen? First, she faints, and then after her companion leaves in search of a doctor, she' —he nodded at the girl—'screams and begins to act as though I had seduced her which—I repeat—I did not!'

'Yes,' the girl agreed. 'But I had to do that to show you what a fine actress I am. And with Cousin Roxanne here I did have to pretend to faint. You must own that I did that splendidly, too, otherwise you wouldn't have noticed me.'

'No one could fail to notice you, missie,' Signor Fernando said with a sigh. 'And now I'll leave you to seduce this gentleman, for I see the mail coach is just about to leave.'

With that he clapped his hat on his head and departed, leaving Stanwyck alone with the girl. He sought momentary fortification from his snuffbox.

'Do you have a name?' he enquired as they went back into the coffee-room.

'Yes, though I must warn you that it is odious.'

He could not help smiling, reminded of one of his nieces. 'How odious?'

'Amanda. Amanda Franklin. Ugh.' She made a face. 'I'd much prefer something exotic, don't you think? Like, well, like Ruby or Heloise!'

'Oh, I think Amanda infinitely prettier than Heloise!'

'Do you really?'

He nodded and smiled at the impudent face. 'Did you really do everything that Signor Fernando accused you of?'

Her head dropped, but only for a minute. 'Yes,' she admitted. 'I regret none of it except for deceiving Cousin Roxanne, but I had to get Signor Fernando's attention.'

'You succeeded there at least,' he said, closing his snuffbox with the flick of a thumbnail.

'Much good it did me!' She frowned. 'If only he would grant me the chance, I know I would be a splendid actress.'

'Amanda, are you feeling more the thing?' A tall lady entered the coffee-room. This, Stanwyck deduced as he rose to his feet, must be Amanda's cousin. Not as pretty as Amanda and rather older, only to be expected in a chaperon, she wore the unmistakable look of respectability.

Blondes, of course, were the current rage, and her colouring was at a disadvantage with brown hair falling

in soft waves to her shoulders. Her creamy complexion
set off a face distinguished by penetrating green eyes, a
full and generous mouth and a rather aristocratic little
nose. A bit of a long Meg rather than a bona-fide Beauty,
he decided to himself, although he had seen worse in the
hallowed rooms of Almack's. She was also, he noted
with considerable astonishment, carrying a gum plaster.

'Roxanne, I want you to meet Mr...' Amanda came
to a halt, looking abashed. 'How odd. I don't even know
your name, sir.'

'Elcot,' the Marquis said, furnishing his family name
as he extended his hand to Amanda's companion. 'Nigel
Elcot. Ma'am, your most obedient.'

'I am Roxanne Franklin, Mr Elcot,' Roxanne replied,
shaking hands with him in a friendly but rather absent-
minded way.

She relinquished his hand almost at once, which was
something of a jolt to Stanwyck who had had more than
one female seize his hand at a ball and refuse to let it
go.

'I couldn't find a doctor, Amanda,' Roxanne said now
to her. 'All the landlord would do was hand me a gum
plaster. He seemed in terror of another guest who had
just ordered a sumptuous luncheon.'

'It doesn't matter,' Amanda told her. 'Signor
Fernando says I have the most promising future for the
stage.'

'Did he?' Roxanne asked. She gazed about the room.
'Where is he?'

'On the mail coach to London, but he told me to be
sure and call on him there.'

A tiny frown appeared on Roxanne's brow. 'Are you
certain of that?' she quizzed.

'Perhaps he didn't say so in so many words, but the intent was unmistakable, wasn't it, sir?' Amanda appealed to Stanwyck, who was watching the exchange with greater interest than he would have believed.

'My dear child,' he said now, 'I shan't support you in so outrageous a whisker!'

Amanda stamped her foot. 'I am not a child.'

Stanwyck continued to look amused.

'Amanda, do try for a little conduct,' Roxanne implored. 'The gentleman will think you wholly ragmannered.'

These words put an end to the foot-stamping but not to a pretty pout that had blossomed. 'I am not a child,' Amanda repeated, looking mulish. 'I'm all of sixteen. Tell him so, Roxanne.'

'And wild to a fault,' the Marquis observed. 'If you have charge of her, ma'am, you have my complete sympathy.'

Roxanne could not repress a laugh, even though she knew it was unseemly to react like that to a stranger.

'What a rude thing to say,' Amanda said. 'And I was just beginning to like you!'

'Now, Amanda, that is quite enough from you,' Roxanne said firmly.

Amanda flushed and lapsed into silence, enabling the Marquis to enquire if the two were any relation to General Franklin. They turned out to be his granddaughters.

'Do you know the general well?' Roxanne asked curiously. She did not think her grandfather, a stodgy stick-in-the-mud as Amanda had called him the other day, moved in the same circles as a nonpareil such as this gentleman.

'Our paths do not usually overlap,' the Marquis admitted. 'But we share membership in White's.'

No further opportunity to delve into the Franklin family tree occurred as Lady Haverly, her ablutions now complete, came into the coffee-room looking for her brother.

'Nigel! Here you are. I thought you told me you had arranged for a parlour.'

'Gwendolyn, give me leave to introduce Miss Roxanne Franklin and Miss Amanda Franklin to you. My sister, Lady Haverly.'

Gwendolyn bobbed her head happily at them all. 'Do you wish to eat or not, Nigel?' she asked. 'The landlord was struggling with several platters. I do think it best to have something, for poor Constance may be too occupied with her theatre friends to bother to order any food!'

'Constance?' Amanda exclaimed, abandoning her sulking. 'Are you on your way to Lady Constance Maltby's festival, ma'am?'

'Yes, indeed,' Lady Haverly said good-homouredly. 'Are you?'

'Oh, sir!' Amanda railed. 'How could you keep such a secret from me?'

'Amanda,' Roxanne exclaimed, trying to hush her and blushing furiously.

'Amanda is quite enamoured of the theatre,' Nigel explained to his sister.

'Oh, are you?' Lady Haverly asked sympathetically.

'I have an idea. Why don't you come to the festival with us? Lady Con doesn't stand on ceremony. I'm sure two more would scarcely be noticed,' Stanwyck said. He looked at his sister. 'Am I right, Gwen?'

Lady Haverly, a bit surprised by this invitation, none the less warmly echoed her brother's sentiments.

'We couldn't do such a thing,' Roxanne protested. 'Amanda and I are on our way to London.'

'Unless you wish to spend your journey dealing with someone in a prolonged state of the sulks,' the Marquis pointed out, 'I'd advise you to come to Brumley with us.'

'But our plans...'

'Have you made arrangements to make London by tonight?' he asked.

She shook her head. 'No, I'd allowed for one night on the road. We meant to stay the night here and then go on to London tomorrow.'

'The only ones in London are the servants,' Amanda pointed out. 'That's if Grandfather has remembered to engage any! Please, Cousin Roxanne, Signor Fernando's troupe will be there, and the jugglers, and well, everything!'

Roxanne shook her head. 'No, that is quite impossible. You are civil to take an interest in us, Mr Elcot, but my answer is no.'

Lady Haverly directed a mild look of enquiry at her brother. 'Stanwyck? What sort of hoax is this?'

'You called him Stanwyck,' Amanda said. 'That wouldn't be the Marquis of Stanwyck, would it?'

'I know he doesn't act like a marquis,' Lady Haverly acknowledged deploringly. 'And it's a pity that the title must pass to him, but such is the case. He *is* the marquis.'

'But I thought your name was Elcot,' Roxanne said.

'So it is.' Stanwyck smiled. 'A man may have many names. Will you reconsider your decision now that you know my position?'

Roxanne shook her head again. 'No, my lord. Your rank makes no difference to me. We must still decline your civil invitation.'

'As you wish,' he replied politely, conscious of considerable vexation. He was not about to seduce either of them, particularly with his sister at hand. 'Well, Gwen, I believe you said our lunch awaited?'

CHAPTER TWO

THE JOURNEY from Wiltshire to London took the better part of a day, and by the time Roxanne at last reached her destination she was fagged to death, a condition induced not only by the inevitable rigours of travel by mail coach but by her companion's tendency to scold her for not having allowed them to attend the festival with the Marquis.

Roxanne was beginning to wonder if being a chaperon to Amanda would be as amusing as she had thought it would be. Certainly she had had no hesitation in taking up the task when her grandfather had written to her, directing her to accompany Amanda to London after Amanda's fourth decampment from Miss Thompson's School.

At the time Roxanne had been trying to quieten her sister Ernestine's squalling babe while Lionel, the five-year-old, had been stepping on the cat's tail, and the idea of being out of Ernestine's household for even a little while was akin to bliss. Not that she was ungrateful to Ernestine for providing her with a roof over her head, but she had often wondered what her life might have been if her father had not become an invalid five years before, necessitating her nursing him through his last years.

She did not begrudge a moment of those years, for who else could dear Papa have relied on. Ernestine did not have the temperament to nurse an invalid. And it *was* civil of her to have invited Roxanne to stay with her

19

after Papa's death a year ago, even though she sometimes wondered if her sister had tendered the invitation
only to gain an unpaid servant to her household.

Now, however, she shook off such unworthy thoughts
and gazed about the house that General Franklin had
rented for them. The establishment was located in
Curzon Street, hardly the fashionable section of town,
but Roxanne knew they were lucky to get anything so
late in the Season. She quibbled neither with its location
nor with the hastily assembled staff that consisted of
Pynne, a rather ancient butler, Pierre the cook, and two
maids, Jennie and Kate.

It was true, as Amanda had pointed out, that the
rooms were small and there was just the one parlour,
but she doubted that they would need grander quarters
since it was unlikely that they would be entertaining any
callers except the general. And as for the furniture, which
Amanda had stigmatised as gothic, Roxanne considered
it all perfectly adequate for their needs.

'The only thing which gave me a moment's pause,'
she confessed to her grandfather's solicitor, Mr Skittles,
when he called during their first week in London, 'was
whether the maids would leave before our first night was
over.'

'Why is that, ma'am?' Mr Skittles, as thin as a reed,
possessed an Adam's apple that bobbed alarmingly
whenever he spoke. He had engaged the servants himself.
'Have you found fault with them?'

'Heavens, no!' Roxanne said quickly, putting down
her teacup. 'Jennie does very well for me. It's Kate.'

'Unsatisfactory?'

'No. But I wouldn't have blamed her if she gave notice
that first night. Amanda's demands!' she explained with
a sigh. 'First she must look like Mrs Siddons, then the

next minute the Countess Lieven, and finally Caro Lamb.'

'Has Kate given notice, then?' Mr Skittles asked, already turning his mind to a replacement.

'No. Actually she might have, but the two share a bond. Kate, we have discovered, is very nearly as stage-struck as Amanda. So nothing could be more providential. I just hope the two of them don't join forces and run off with a theatre company. You've finished your tea. Do take another cup, and perhaps another biscuit?'

Mr Skittles acquiesced in having his cup refilled and recalled the purpose behind his call. 'Actually, Miss Franklin, I've had some news of your grandfather. He is in France, as you know, and should be arriving within the week.'

'That quickly?' Roxanne asked. She had hoped for more time in London. She had a plan for her own future which must be settled before she could present it to her grandfather.

'He has given me leave to establish your credit with several London shops and has left a certain sum at your disposal. Not a large amount,' he said hastily as the hopeful look bloomed on her face.

Roxanne gave a disappointed sigh. 'Of course not. I fear poor Grandfather is nearly as far up the River Tick as Amanda and I.'

Mr Skittles was shocked at so blunt an assessment of his client's financial straits.

'You can rest assured that I shan't beggar poor Grandfather,' Roxanne went on, 'but I did want to take Amanda about and see the sights. Perhaps Somerset House and St Paul's.'

'There can be no problem there,' Mr Skittles assured her. 'And should you need any help whatsoever, do feel free to call on me.'

'There is one thing, Mr Skittles. Perchance you are acquainted with the Marquis of Stanwyck?'

'Stanwyck? Hardly acquainted, ma'am, but I do know of him.'

'A loose screw, I suppose?'

Mr Skittles looked aghast. 'Heavens, no, he's unexceptionable! A leader of the ton. A veritable nonpareil.' The praises could not roll off Mr Skittles's tongue with any greater speed. 'I don't think him impervious to females, but he's not a loose screw. Why do you ask? Are you acquainted with him?'

'I've met him.'

'Indeed? His friendship can win you entrée into the highest circles.'

'I am not a friend of his,' Roxanne protested, and even if she were to gain entrée into the highest circles she was not exactly sure she would know what to do then. Still, it was sobering to think that she had practically accused Stanwyck of being an unscrupulous sort. She would apologise the next time they met.

But what am I thinking of? she asked herself. Stanwyck did not run in her circles, so she would have little opportunity to see him again. The old adage of opportunity knocking on one's door came to her mind. Stanwyck had knocked, and she had briskly sent him about his business!

'You have been most kind, Mr Skittles,' Roxanne said. 'I wonder if you might know of a respectable family hereabouts in need of a governess.'

'A governess, Miss Franklin?' Mr Skittles frowned, his surprise evident. 'Are you planning to become a governess?'

She gave an emphatic nod. 'I've been considering it for some time,' she confessed. Almost as soon as she had taken up residence with Ernestine!

'Does the general know of your plans?' The solicitor's Adam's apple was bobbing furiously.

Roxanne shook her head. 'Poor Grandfather would have an attack of apoplexy if I ever suggested such a thing. That's why I hope the matter to be a *fait accompli* by the time he returns to London.' She paused, noticing the look of scepticism on Mr Skittle's face. 'I am quite in earnest, I assure you. If you do know of any families in need of a governess...'

'Of course, Miss Franklin, of course,' Mr Skittles said hastily, temporarily passing over the notion of just what the general, a high stickler in matters of female propriety, would do and say if he ever found his granddaughter a governess in someone's household.

Despite his misgivings, Mr Skittles dutifully ferreted out the information about who might want a governess, and a few days later Roxanne set off on a round of interviews. Her first call was on Lord and Lady Lally, who desired a governess for their three incorrigible offspring, all male. The boys, ranging in age from six to twelve, greeted Roxanne by hurling a snake from the top of the Adam stairs. The Lallys, in Roxanne's opinion, needed a zoo-keeper, not a governess.

Her second call was on Lady Ogilvie, who at sixty-three was far removed from needing a governess. Her need was rather for a companion who would help her to dose herself by fetching the many vials of medication and potions set to cure whatever was the fashionable ailment of the week. Roxanne had only a half-hour interview with the woman, but learned that Lady Ogilvie suffered not only from the grippe and influenza but also from gout and dyspepsia.

Her third interview was with Mr Justin Cartier, who needed a governess for his nine-year-old twin daughters. Mr Cartier was a handsome and haughty individual who made her feel a veritable nobody, despite her very best walking-dress. He questioned her closely, looked her over with some condescension, and offered no protest to the salary she named. She left his residence feeling slightly uneasy. She had half accused Stanwyck of being a rake. Mr Cartier was, she felt, the real thing. Clearly the path to the secure future she had envisioned as a governess was rife with obstacles.

Two days later, the Marquis, elegantly garbed in a coat of Bath-blue superfine, his cravat expertly tied à l'Orientale, Hessians polished to an eye-blinding gloss, drove his high-perch phaeton to the residence of Mrs Kinney.

He had tired of the festival and posted back to London, but it was not to be expected that so temperamental a favourite as Fanny would greet him with the ardour of Penelope for her wayward Ulysses. Even so, he was a trifle surprised at the coolness of his reception.

'How is this, Nigel?' she asked, as he strolled unannounced into her dressing-room on Thursday morning. 'Can you give me no warning of your coming?'

'Don't be missish, Fanny,' he said, mildly amused at her attempt to wrap the Chinese dressing-gown tightly about her person. She looked as though she had just come from bed. 'I've seen you in déshabille before,' he reminded her. He paused, struck by a scent in the air, and gave a judicious sniff. 'Does my nose deceive me, or is that a new scent? Quite intriguing.'

'I'm glad you like it, Nigel,' she said, turning back to the mirror in front of her and dipping her fingers into her rouge-pots.

She did look bewitching with her dark hair hanging in lustrous curls, her eyes just as black and heavily lashed, and a mouth that was as quick to wear a pout as a smile.

'How is that odious aunt of yours?' she asked now as he stripped off his York tan gloves.

'As odious as ever,' he answered with aplomb.

'I thought you would be gone for at least a week.'

'I cut my visit short,' he said, putting his arms about her waist and kissing her willowy neck. 'Aren't you glad?'

'Of course,' she said, continuing to rouge her cheeks. 'But I had plans for the day. Viscount Webbe has been obliging enough to visit me in your absence. He invited me for a drive to Richmond Park.'

If Mrs Kinney had hoped to strike a jealous chord in Stanwyck's breast, she was out of luck, for his face showed no trace of feeling. The Marquis, ever since his disappointment with Drusilla Crosby, had never felt the slightest pang of jealousy over any other female. He drew away from her now and meticulously wiped his hands on a handkerchief, explaining that her new scent was too sweet for his tastes. 'If you are promised to Webbe, I'd best not detain you,' he said. 'He is such a punctual fellow, and no doubt shall beat down the door.'

Mrs Kinney turned, already half regretting her show of temper. 'I could be free this evening, Nigel,' she said, as he moved toward the doorway.

His eyes met hers for a moment. 'I shall keep that in mind, Fanny,' he said smoothly, and strolled out.

He walked back to his phaeton, absorbed in thoughts about his three-month liaison with Fanny, wondering if it were better to give her her *congé* now before she could do it to him. He was just about to climb into his vehicle when a breathless voice hailed him.

'Oh, sir, Lord Stanwyck! It is you, isn't it, sir?'

He turned, wondering who could address him in such a fashion, and found Amanda Franklin smiling up at him.

'Good morning, Miss Franklin.' He made her a punctilious bow.

'Good morning. How lucky we are to encounter you,' she said, speaking for herself and her maid, who was standing gawking up at the Marquis.

Stanwyck had cut his wisdoms and was not deceived by the innocent face she turned to him. 'Don't pitch that gammon at me,' he told her. 'And where is your cousin?'

'If you mean Roxanne, she's at home in Curzon Street.'

'Safe in the knowledge that you are racketing about town?' he quizzed, and knew that he had scored a hit as she flushed.

'I told her I was bound for Hookham's, and indeed I was. Only...'

He eyed her. 'Only?' he prompted.

'Only I went to your residence in Berkeley Square instead, thinking to see if you were in,' Amanda said, making a clean breast of it. 'And you were just pulling out in your carriage, so I called up a hack and Kate and I followed you here. We've been waiting for you to emerge.'

'Good heavens!' He pushed back his high-crowned beaver felt. 'Why did you wish to do such a foolish thing?'

She gazed innocently up at him. 'I thought you might be paying a call on Mrs Kinney, since you just arrived last evening.'

The Marquis's brows lifted a fraction of an inch. 'And what do you know of Mrs Kinney, my girl?'

'I know that she is your *chère amie*, and I don't think it anything to be ashamed about. I think it's splendid that you have an actress for your mistress. I don't mean to give offence,' she said as he frowned. 'But I thought you might be so kind as to introduce me to her, for she has acted in London and knows people.'

'How did you know of my arrival?' he asked.

'Kate, here' —she nodded at her maid who dipped a curtsy to the Marquis—'has a cousin who is a down-stairs maid in your establishment. She told us you had returned. And you did pay a call on Mrs Kinney, didn't you? Oh, sir, would you introduce me?'

'My dear girl, you forget yourself!' Stanwyck declared.

She took a step back, looking abashed. 'Oh, pray don't be offended. I didn't think you'd mind, even though Roxanne did say that you were only amusing yourself by being kind to us in Wiltshire. I suppose it was a coming thing to ask.' She turned and began to walk away with Kate.

Stanwyck stared at the two hunched figures and twisted his lips. 'Not so fast, Miss Amanda,' he called. His long stride made short work of the distance between them.

'You needn't be concerned with me and my stupid af-fairs,' Amanda said.

'Very true, but I choose to be.' He turned her about gently to face him and noticed the brimming eyes. 'No, don't turn into a watering-pot. It ain't your style. Let me take you back to where you are staying.'

'Do you mean it?' The tears in her eyes melted instantly. 'In your phaeton?' All signs of the dismals had gone.

'Well, not in a hack,' he retorted with a smile that took the sting from his words. He helped her and Kate into the carriage.

'I've never ridden in a high-perch phaeton like this,' Amanda gasped minutes later as he took the corner without a break in speed.

'I should hope not,' Stanwyck replied, thinking of the specifications he had given his carriage-maker. There was not another phaeton like it in the kingdom.

'Sir, are you a member of the Four Horse Club?'

'Yes,' he acknowledged reluctantly. 'But how do you know of such things? Don't tell me my downstairs maid hàs been prattling about that!'

'Oh, no,' Amanda said, while Kate clung to her arm as they rounded a bend. 'We read about you in the papers of the *Morning Post* and the *Gazette*.'

'Really? Nothing too scandalous, I hope?'

'Is it true that you and Mr Philip Dudley have a wager of a hundred pounds on the next offspring of Sir Greg Martingale?' Amanda asked. 'Mr Dudley maintaining it would be red-haired while you say black?'

'Yes,' Stanwyck said, much struck as he recalled the bet fashioned at White's the night before his departure for his aunt's. 'Do you mean that Lady Martingale is delivered of her child?'

'Yes,' Amanda informed him, pleased that she could perform this task. 'And the *Morning Post* says that Mr Dudley is frantic because Sir Greg won't allow him into the nursery to determine the colour of the hair.'

'Oh, Greg shan't object to *my* seeing the babe,' Stanwyck said, pulling his carriage to a dead stop at the entrance she had indicated at the very last minute.

'Won't you come in?' Amanda asked after the three of them lurched forward, then back. 'I know Cousin Roxanne will be pleased to see you.'

He had intended to decline the invitation when the door to the residence opened and Justin Cartier emerged, looking grim.

'Hallo, Stanwyck,' he said, surprised to see the Marquis's carriage. 'Back in London, I see.'

'For the moment,' Stanwyck agreed, wondering what the likes of Cartier—a notoriously loose screw—could have to do with the Franklins. He decided to accept Amanda's invitation.

'Do you know that man?' he asked Amanda as they went in.

'Never saw him before,' was Amanda's reply as she skipped into the parlour where Roxanne sat frowning over her embroidery. 'Roxanne, Lord Stanwyck is here!'

'Lord Stanwyck!' Roxanne exclaimed. 'Good heavens, it is *you*! I mean . . . I beg your pardon.'

'I was fortunate enough to encounter Miss Amanda during my round of calls this morning,' Stanwyck explained with a smile. 'I gave her a ride home.'

'Cousin Roxanne, you must see his phaeton,' Amanda said, dragging her cousin from the sofa to the window which overlooked the drive. 'It was the most exhilarating ride I've ever experienced.'

'Your cattle certainly look like prime articles,' Roxanne said. 'Welsh breds, I presume?'

He nodded, surprised. 'You have an eye for horse-flesh, Miss Franklin.'

She laughed away the compliment. 'Heavens, no! Father just used to say Welsh breds were *de rigueur* for any nonpareil.'

'Too kind, Miss Franklin.' He seated himself next to her on the sofa. 'Between you and Miss Amanda I shall be even more high in the instep than usual.'

'Sir,' Amanda interrupted. 'Do you think I might drive your phaeton?'

The Marquis blinked. There were limits to his good nature. 'No, you may not,' he said roundly. 'You'd probably break your neck. And I do not intend to don sackcloth and ashes. Deuced uncomfortable, I hear!'

Roxanne swallowed a laugh. 'Do stop teasing Lord Stanwyck,' she told Amanda. 'I do hope, sir, you will share our luncheon.'

He lifted a brow. 'You are being most civil, Miss Franklin.'

She blushed, knowing full well what he was referring to. 'Pray forgive me; when last we met, I was not aware. That is, I did know who you were since you did tell me, but I didn't know what you were. Does that make sense?'

'Yes!' he said. 'As Gwen put it, you didn't know me from Adam and were prudent not to be taken in by a stranger. And now that we are no longer strangers, I shall accept your invitation.'

Soon enough they were all enjoying a meal of ham, melon and assorted cheeses.

'Did you buy anything at Hookham's, Amanda?' Roxanne asked.

Her question caught Amanda by surprise, and she choked on a wedge of cheese. The Marquis, the closest to her, pounded her vigorously on the back.

'Have some water,' he whispered.

'Hookham's? Oh, Hookham's!' Amanda said, when Roxanne repeated her question. 'Actually, Roxanne, I didn't see any book I wanted.'

Her cousin was taken aback. 'Really? They say it has the largest supply of books in all London. How odd that you found nothing to interest you.'

'Yes, I know,' Amanda said, avoiding the Marquis's knowing eyes. 'But it doesn't matter. I have several issues of *La Belle Assemblée* I can read.'

Taking pity on Amanda, the Marquis smoothly introduced a new topic, namely their coming as his guests to a production at Drury Lane.

'Oh, sir!' Amanda exclaimed.

'Is tomorrow evening too soon? I have a box.'

A tiny frown knitted Roxanne's brow. 'An evening performance?'

'Oh, Cousin Roxanne, you can't deny me that!'

'Would a matinée be more the thing for a child of her years?' Stanwyck asked, meeting Roxanne's pensive gaze.

'No, it would not,' Amanda said, looking much put out. 'And I do wish you would stop calling me a child. I am all of sixteen.'

'Quiet, minx,' he ordered. 'I am addressing your cousin.'

Amanda turned imploring eyes to her cousin. 'Roxanne, please?'

Roxanne felt her resolve weaken. 'I suppose just this once, since we will be Lord Stanwyck's guests. But you must promise to behave.'

'Oh, I shall, I shall!' Amanda said. 'Thank you both.' She hugged them and dashed off, saying she was too excited to consume another morsel and must tell Kate the good news.

CHAPTER THREE

WONDERING if the Marquis would think her family wholly rag-mannered, Roxanne hastened to apologise for Amanda's exuberance.

The Marquis laughed off her words. 'I find her easy display of good spirits refreshing. And let me assure you that the evening performance won't be so bad.'

'I hope not. Although they say the crowd in the pit can get unruly.'

'You won't be in the pit,' he reminded her kindly.

She flushed. 'No, of course not.'

'One thing perplexes me, Miss Franklin. How is that you have charge over Amanda? You can't be but a few years her senior.'

A quick peal of laughter broke out. 'I can see why you are a prime favourite with the ladies, Lord Stanwyck. Such gallantry must please. I don't mind revealing to you that I am five and twenty. And my charge of Amanda is merely temporary. The teachers at Miss Thompson's School were in flat despair.'

'Prone to mischief-making, your Amanda?' Stanwyck asked.

Roxanne nodded. 'I believe that final straw was her attempt to convince the dancing-master that they should go off to Vienna and see how the waltz ought to be danced!'

'I can just see the little minx doing such a thing.' The Marquis chuckled. 'May I ask after her parents?'

Roxanne sobered. 'She has none. Her mother died at her birth, and her father broke his neck in a carriage accident soon after. Amanda has been at school or under the tutelage of a succession of governesses. When the problem at the school arose and it seemed necessary to remove Amanda—the headmistress said that she would lead the rest of the girls into a state of rebellion!— Grandfather asked me to accompany her to London.'

'An act of considerable courage. I'd sooner volunteer for the Peninsula,' the Marquis said.

Her shoulders shook with laughter. 'It's really not so arduous, I assure you. Amanda can be exasperating, I admit, but what else can one expect if everyone about her is pinching and scolding her? In general, relations have been cordial between us.'

'Due to your own equable temperament,' he said. 'Does nothing overset you?'

She was surprised by this query, but read nothing but kindly interest in his eyes. Her answer came readily enough. 'Hardly anything, I dare say. Roxanne, the rock, my father used to tease me.' She smiled at the memory. 'But really I have never understood the sense of flying into the boughs when a quiet talking through of the matter would suffice.'

'Would that more of your sex adopted such a sensible strategy,' he said. 'Is Amanda to make her come-out this Season?'

'Heavens, no!' Roxanne was shocked at such a notion. 'She is far too green. We will just have a little time in London before our futures will be decided.'

He cocked his head at her. 'I see why Amanda's future must be decided, but I can't understand why yours must be as well.'

'I suppose you wouldn't, unless you knew how things were.'

'And how are things with you?' he asked.

He was a veritable stranger, and the question was a personal one, but Roxanne was not reluctant to confide in him.

'My father died a year ago; ever since, I've lived with my sister Ernestine. I'm not ungrateful to her for taking me in, but I did think that while in London I might find a position as a governess or set up a school of my own. I have the learning necessary.'

'Your family approves of this venture?'

'They don't know a thing about it,' she confessed. 'I've never told a soul before you! Grandfather would undoubtedly oppose the idea of my earning my own keep, but since he is in Paris at the moment, I thought I might have the future settled before he returned to London.'

'And what about Amanda?'

'If I start a school, she might help me.'

He blenched. 'Miss Franklin, I can readily envision you in the role of a governess or schoolteacher, but when you speak of Amanda taking command of a schoolroom...'

She was convulsed in giggles. 'Yes, I dare say you are right about that!'

'On my way in I couldn't help but notice that you had a visitor,' he said, sipping a glass of sherry. 'Are you acquainted with Mr Cartier?'

'We met the other day.' She frowned as she recalled that interview.

'A suitor of yours?'

She stared. 'Good Jupiter, no! In fact, he's more in the way of being a prospective employer. My grandfather's secretary told me of several who might be hiring a governess. Mr Cartier's name was among them. I saw him first a few days ago, and he called today to offer to double the salary I had asked for.'

The Marquis pursed his lips. 'Twice the salary?'

She nodded. 'I was thunderstruck. He has only the two daughters, and while I was not disposed to like him much before...'

'You have suffered a change of mind now?' he concluded.

She pondered the words carefully, then shook her head. 'No, my feelings have not altered, but the salary, I own, is tempting.'

'Miss Franklin, you're new in London, so I hope you'll forgive my presumption in poking my nose into what don't concern me. I'd advise you in this instance to follow your first instincts with regard to Mr Cartier.'

A look of understanding flashed across her face. 'Then he is a rake?'

'Among other faults, I believe, he possesses a disposition toward foisting his attentions on the females in his household, which accounts for his being in habitual need of a governess for his daughters.'

He had wondered how she would react to such plain speaking, but noted with approval that she did not resort to missishness.

She nodded her head. 'I'm glad you told me this, Lord Stanwyck.'

'Have you no other prospects besides Mr Cartier?'

'Oh, yes,' she said cheerfully. 'Lady Ogilvie is seeking a companion.'

'Whom she will undoubtedly nag to death!' he retorted. 'Loath though I am to say it, your grandfather's secretary seems to have been of no great assistance, if all of his prospects are like Lady Ogilvie and Mr Cartier.

I have several friends with children, and shall find a household where you can be happy.'

She managed to stammer out her thanks, to which he paid not the slightest heed, and then after finishing the last of a bowl of strawberries, he departed, leaving Roxanne wondering at his generosity and then, more idiotishly, what it would be like to ride in his high-perch phaeton.

'Oh, Cousin Roxanne, isn't it too thrilling? Drury Lane with the Marquis! I vow I could burst from excitement,' Amanda said the next morning at Curzon Street.

'Then you would miss the performance tonight,' Roxanne pointed out. 'And do stop prancing about,' she pleaded, as Amanda danced away from the four-poster bed and towards the mirror. 'And do tell me which of these two dresses you prefer to wear tonight.'

Amanda halted and wrinkled her nose. 'They are both hideous, but I expect that that one'—she pointed to a yellow muslin—'is less hideous than the other. Oh, Roxanne, can't we order new gowns?'

'Even if we did, I doubt that they would be ready by tonight,' Roxanne said. She laid the yellow dress on Amanda's bed. 'It's not so hideous. Kate can press it.'

Amanda bounced on the bed. 'Drury Lane! Lord Stanwyck is so obliging, I vow I forgive him for being so disobliging about introducing me to Mrs Kinney yesterday.'

Roxanne looked aghast. 'Mrs Kinney?' she exclaimed. 'Amanda, what have you been up to?'

'Nothing,' Amanda said hastily, trying to retrieve the slip. 'I just happened to be near her residence when Lord Stanwyck emerged, that's all.'

'That's all!' Roxanne eyed her reprovingly. 'So you were nowhere near Hookham's!'

'But the Marquis didn't introduce me to her, so there's nothing to scold me about,' Amanda said hastily. 'And anyway, Kate's cousin who works for Stanwyck says that Mrs Kinney will not be enjoying his patronage much longer.'

'You mustn't listen to *on-dits*,' Roxanne chided before her own curiosity got the better of her. 'How does she know that?'

'He's growing bored,' Amanda explained, twirling a strand of hair about a finger absent-mindedly. 'The servants know the signs because he's had so many mistresses. None has lasted more than two months before. I dare say it all comes from wearing the willow for Drusilla Crosby.'

Roxanne put down the yellow muslin dress. 'Who?'

Amanda stared at Roxanne. 'Roxanne, don't you know anything?'

'I don't have the access you have to Kate's cousin.'

'Oh, Kate didn't tell me about Drusilla. I knew that ages ago in school. It occurred years and years ago,' Amanda said, assuming a wise pose on the bed. 'Stanwyck was just a young man, very wet behind the ears. He fell top over tail in love with Drusilla. She was the leading Beauty that season. She played him along, giving him to believe she would accept his suit—only to accept Robert Goodheart. The Marquis never recovered from the blow. And that is why he flits from mistress to mistress, nursing his wounded heart.'

Roxanne laughed so hard that her ribs ached. 'I saw not a trace of a wounded heart in our parlour!'

'That's because he covers it up so well, don't you think?'

'What I think is that you have read far too many lending-library romances,' she said sternly. 'And I do hope you haven't fallen in love with the Marquis yourself!'

This statement brought about a quick round of giggles from Amanda.

'Roxanne, really! The Marquis is so old. I vow he could be at least thirty!'

Roxanne was tempted to point out that thirty did not mean that the Marquis had one foot in the grave, but she gave up that notion. Amanda at sixteen could never consider anyone over twenty-five as anything but ancient.

'Does Drusilla live in London?' she asked later as they attempted to find a suitable dress in Roxanne's wardrobe.

'No, she lives in America.' Amanda sighed. 'I still think we must get new gowns, Roxanne.'

'It would be a horrid expense just for one evening,' Roxanne replied, looking through her small collection of dresses. Most of them had been purchased years ago and were out of style, but perhaps with an eye to the pages of *La Belle Assemblée* she might be able to alter one of them and appear less *démodée*.

While Roxanne plied needle and thread in this attempt, Stanwyck stood in the middle of his dressing-room staring with furious concentration at his reflection.

Two steps behind him stood Michaels, his valet, watching with bated breath as the Marquis twisted the linen cloth dextrously about his neck and gave it a final pat of satisfaction.

'That will do!'

'Yes, indeed, my lord,' Michaels agreed.

Satisfied that he looked presentable, Nigel descended the Adam stairs, pausing momentarily to survey the morning mail on the silver tray at the bottom. One missive bore the unmistakable scent of Fanny. As he debated whether to break the seal, the knocker on his door sounded sharply, and before the butler could reach it, it sounded loudly once again.

Wondering who the impatient caller might be, Stanwyck took a step towards the door, which Vance, the butler, had now opened, and the two men were nearly knocked flat by the entrance of the Honourable Andrew Finch-William, Lord and Lady Haverly's firstborn.

'Uncle Nigel! Thank God you're here,' Andrew said. He was a sturdy fair-haired lad who had reached his twenty-first birthday only two months previously.

'Where else ought I to be?' the Marquis asked mildly. 'It's only eleven o'clock. And, my word, what kind of rig do you have on? You look as though you've slept in that coat!'

Andrew gave a mirthless laugh. 'No chance of that. I haven't had any sleep at all.'

The Marquis had already taken in the ringed eyes and faint stubble that along with the dishevelled clothes could mean only one thing in a young man of Andrew's years.

'You've been up all night at the green baize tables.' It was a statement, not a question.

Andrew nodded.

The Marquis sighed. 'Come along to the breakfast-room. You can tell me all about it there.'

'I don't need food, Uncle Nigel!'

'Perhaps not, but I do,' Stanwyck replied and thrust the younger man into the breakfast-room.

'Uncle Nigel, I'm in a bit of a muddle,' Andrew said as he sat down.

'So I deduce,' Stanwyck said calmly, 'or you would never appear in public with your cravat untied.' He placed a plate of muffins and ham in front of him, commanding him to eat.

Obediently Andrew complied.

'Let me hazard a guess,' Nigel said. 'You've run through your allowance, and your pockets are to let.'

'Yes.'

'And since you don't wish to apply to your father—fathers are so deuced unfeeling, aren't they?—you came to me. And quite right to do so. I'll advance you whatever you need.'

'I don't think even you can do that,' Andrew said gloomily.

The Marquis put down his fork. 'In that deep? The members of White's don't play for chicken stakes, do they?'

'If it were only White's,' Andrew said hollowly.

Stanwyck's head shot up. 'Not Watier's?'

Andrew nodded.

Stanwyck swore, wondering if he ought to ring a peal over young Andrew, but the unhappy face across from him spoke volumes and he was reminded of his own foolish youth.

'Buck up, lad,' he said now. 'Everyone gets scorched now and then. Tell me the sum, but mind I'll have you pay back every penny!'

'It's not money, Uncle Nigel.'

'You mean you didn't lose a vast amount?'

'Oh, I did,' Andrew agreed. 'But in the end I didn't have any money left to wager, and my luck was turning. Since Lord Owen wouldn't accept my vowels, I put up something else in place of money.'

Nigel sighed. 'By heaven, what is it then? Not the sapphire ring your father gave you for your come-out? He'd tear your hair out if you lost that.'

'No, I did think of it,' he confessed, 'but I decided against it.'

'Well, then?' Stanwyck asked, waiting.

Andrew cast his eyes down to his plate, then back up to his uncle.

'I've lost the hunting-box Uncle William bequeathed to me!'

CHAPTER FOUR

'THE HUNTING-BOX!' Stanwyck expostulated as he threw down his napkin. 'What a caulker!'

His uncle, Mr William Elcot, had willed the hunting-box to young Andrew. Located in a prime area of Derbyshire, it was the envy of several notables who throughout the years had attempted in vain to purchase it from the family.

'I know I fully deserve to have my hair combed!' Andrew said in a small voice.

'You deserve to have your neck wrung!' Stanwyck said witheringly. 'Gwen was cast in alt that her son had in-herited it. William took a liking to you when you were an angelic-looking babe of nine months. Thank your stars he never clapped eyes on you again. And now you've lost it gaming! Why, in heaven?'

'I told you, Uncle Nigel. My luck was turning. I was certain of it.'

His uncle snorted. 'Better to have lost the sapphire ring. Well,' he demanded, 'what are you going to do about it?'

Andrew met his eyes nervously. 'I thought you might advise me. I can't possibly tell Father how the land lies. He said one more scrape, and I'd be packed off to Haveril.'

'Then buy it back,' the Marquis said promptly. 'I'll put up the sum. We can't have the property fall into the hands of anyone out of the family.'

'It may be rather dear,' Andrew warned.

42

'I think I have ample funds to secure its return,' Stanwyck said drily.

Andrew looked abashed. 'I went round to see Lord Owen this morning and wasn't even allowed in the door.'

Stanwyck smiled. 'A ploy to drive up your considerable anxiety, as well as the price. Oh, save the hangdog look! I'll call on Owen and settle the matter, if you like.'

Andrew brightened immediately. 'Would you, sir? I would be so grateful.'

'I'll send you word later on how the matter fares,' Stanwyck promised. 'And since I am being such a font of wisdom this morning, I'd advise you to get some sleep and in the future to eschew the play at Watier's!'

This stricture was humbly accepted by Andrew as his due, and he went off looking as though a burden had been lifted from his shoulders. The Marquis finished his breakfast. Andrew was a good boy, but the exuberance of his youth had led to the inevitable trial at Watier's tables. That was only to be expected.

Stanwyck himself remembered a scrape or two from his own salad days. Since he was already up, and the matter was on his mind, he decided to attend to it at once.

He called at Owen's, finding as his nephew had predicted that the owner was absent. A brief search amid the familiar haunts of Manton's and Cribb's parlour failed to elicit the gentleman in question, and Stanwyck was beginning to wonder if Owen had vanished off the face of the earth, when he suddenly remembered the peer's addiction to good health. In some circles he was considered something of a crank. Owen's regimen included a brisk swim daily in the Serpentine, weather permitting. In pursuit of his quarry, the Marquis drove to the Park, where he found Owen just concluding a dip in the lake.

'A word with you, Lord Owen, if you don't mind,' he said as the older man dried himself.

'Stanwyck, ain't it?' Owen squinted at him. 'Capital day! It's this fresh air and a swim! Invigorates the blood. Come down from the horse and try it yourself.'

The Marquis repressed a shiver of horror. 'Perhaps another time,' he said. 'A bit cold for me.'

'B—Bosh, don't be an old woman,' Owen said, his teeth chattering.

'I'd like to redeem that hunting-box you won from my nephew,' Stanwyck said, as Owen struggled into his clothes.

'Can't,' the older man grunted.

The Marquis was prepared for such a statement. 'You may name your price.'

Owen shook his white head, sprinkling water liberally on Nigel. 'I'd like to help, but I can't. I don't have the hunting-box.' He buttoned his waistcoat. 'I had a rum bit of luck myself. No one's been pressing me, but after I won that hunting-box from your nevvie, bless me if Webbe doesn't stroll up. He'd seen the action at the tables.' Owen scowled. 'I owe him a goodly sum, and the villain demands the hunting-box as payment. I didn't like to do it, but I was driven to the wall!'

Stanwyck's brows knit as he absorbed the full meaning of the other man's words. 'Webbe has the hunting-box?'

Owen nodded. 'And if you mean to broach the matter to him, I'd be a mite careful.'

Stanwyck stared. 'Careful? Is that a warning, sir?'

Owen shrugged. 'Call it what you will. Webbe's jealous of you. I'm not the first to think that.'

The Marquis laughed. 'You misjudge him.'

'No, I don't,' Owen retorted, tying a very creditable Mathematical without benefit of a mirror or valet. 'I know the signs well enough.' He turned to face the Marquis. 'He's a case of the green-eyed monster, sure enough. Keep in mind that he only came into his title two years ago and quite by chance. Who would have thought his uncle and two cousins would pop off that way! Those are the ones who are always anxious to take the lead in the ton. Only in his case he sees you as the premier figure—being one of Gentleman Jack's prize pupils and a prime favourite with the Patronesses.'

'Do spare my blushes, Owen!' Stanwyck besought him.

Owen laughed, and clapped him on the shoulder. 'You know your worth better than I.'

'I also know that Webbe is uncommonly good looking, the Patronesses dote on him, and Jackson has given him personal instruction.'

Owen conceded these points. 'That merely fuels the fire. Think how much more attention he'd harvest if you weren't about. He'd be the premier Corinthian then, wouldn't he?'

'Is he planning to murder me?' Stanwyck asked derisively.

'No, but he'll take any chance to show you to disadvantage. He's been squiring Mrs Kinney about in your absence.'

'So I understand, but then Mrs Kinney has never been the sort to languish at home when she could be spreading her charms about. And Webbe's always seemed civil enough to me when we met.'

'During your absence it came to a head,' Owen said, now completely restored to respectability in dress. 'Lady Petersham begged his advice on the colour of the walls for her sitting-room. When he'd given it, she then said she'd wait on your return and see what *you* said.'

'Heavens, he'd be a coxcomb to take umbrage at that! Lady Petersham is a widgeon. Everyone knows that. She's forever redecorating her room in the vain hope that good luck will follow.'

'You and I know that,' Owen said sagely, 'but Webbe is one of the younger set. The excesses of youth make for danger, Stanwyck. Heed my words.'

Later, as the Marquis sat in Webbe's green saloon, he could not help thinking that Owen, as was common to gentlemen with more than sixty years in their dish, had mistaken the matter. There was nothing sinister in Webbe's tall, slender figure, meticulously garbed in a white frilled shirt, snowy white cravat and biscuit pantaloons. His features were pleasant, distinguished mainly by a squarish jaw and blond hair cut à la Brutus.

'Stanwyck.' Webbe drawled a greeting and extended two fingers. 'Sorry to keep you waiting. I was mixing snuff.'

'Were you?' Stanwyck asked mildly. 'I trust the mixture was a successful one?'

'You be the judge,' Webbe said, snapping open a Sèvres snuffbox.

The marquis caught the unmistakable aroma of Otto of Roses in the mixture. Although it was the favourite of the Regent, it was not his. But to refuse to try the mixture would be a solecism. He compromised by taking a minuscule pinch between thumb and forefinger. 'Very nice.'

Webbe smiled, and inhaled heartily.

'I'm here on behalf of my nephew,' Stanwyck told the Viscount after the snuff-taking had been completed. 'He lost his hunting-box to Owen last night. Owen tells me you have it now.'

'That's correct,' Webbe said. 'I hold several of Owen's notes. The hunting-box cancels that debt.'

'I am not party to your transaction with Owen, but I should like to redeem the hunting-box. It's been in my family for decades. I believe Uncle William used to say that Henry the Eighth gave it to an ancestor.'

'I may have come into my title only two years ago, Stanwyck, but I understand the importance of family matters,' the Viscount said stiffly. 'There will be a delay until my solicitor can assess its value.'

Stanwyck lifted an eyebrow. 'I wasn't about to cheat you, Webbe.'

The Viscount gave a wintry smile. 'I certainly hope not.'

Stanwyck wondered about the faint challenge he saw in the Viscount's blue eyes. Or was he imagining things because of Owen's warning?

'I was told Andrew put the hunting-box up against a wager of a thousand pounds.'

'Yes, but it's worth considerably more. In fact I have already instructed my solicitor to ride down to Derbyshire to estimate its value. It's in such a prime location that I'm sorely tempted to keep it.' He laughed at the Marquis's rigid stare. 'Just roasting you, Stanwyck. I dare say the family would never rest easy with it in the hands of someone else, would they? I shall be glad for you to redeem it when I know how much it's worth.'

There seemed nothing more to be said. Stanwyck rose to his feet. 'You will notify me when you've settled on a price?'

The Viscount smiled. 'Certainly.'

'I'm acting on behalf of my nephew, Webbe. I would like all communication to be between you and me. I trust you won't bring it to my brother-in-law.'

'As you wish,' Webbe replied, and saw him out with the same odd smile playing on his thin lips.

Tuesday evening arrived not a moment too soon for the impatient Amanda, who had to be dissuaded from craning her neck out of the bedroom window as she waited for the Marquis's carriage.

'And do try for a little conduct,' Roxanne pleaded, smoothing her cousin's dress. 'Your gown is already crushed!'

'I don't care,' Amanda said, giving an impatient hop back to the window. 'Here it comes. Here it comes!' she squealed and, impervious to Roxanne's entreaties, raced out of the room and down the stairs.

Roxanne, although just as excited, followed at a more sedate pace. She had sat in front of the mirror for longer than usual, and Jennie had arranged her hair in the beguiling à l'Anglaise which was a perfect counterpoint to the demure French silk she wore, a dress resurrected from the back of her wardrobe and hastily refurbished with a lace ribbon at the waist and bodice. She hoped it looked new.

'Ah, Miss Franklin.' Stanwyck bowed as she approached. Amanda was already hanging on his arm. He looked as dashing and handsome as ever.

'Shall we?' he asked, extending the other arm to her, and he swept the two ladies out of the door and into his carriage. Sooner than one could utter 'Mr Shakespeare', they were at Drury Lane.

'Sir, sir, is that Edmund Kean?' Amanda asked as they made their way through the crowd to Stanwyck's box.

The Marquis swivelled his head obligingly in the direction Amanda indicated. 'Yes, I believe so.'

'Would you introduce me?'

'Out of the question.'

Amanda took this refusal philosophically. 'They say the Regent is a great admirer of the theatre. Will he be here tonight?'

'I hope not,' the Marquis drawled as he drew the chairs out for his two guests. 'Prinny would spark a riot if he showed his face.'

'Surely not,' Roxanne protested. 'I know that people are rumoured to boo him in public, but still...'

'People are apt to run him out, which is why he wisely hides from public view,' Stanwyck told her. 'And can anyone blame them? He's squandered so much of the public monies satisfying his curious whims with regard to his palace, and now suddenly says it shan't do. He *must* have this new pavilion in Brighton, which is rumoured to cost the earth!'

'It does seem vexatious of him to change his mind so,' Roxanne agreed. 'It puts one in mind of a greedy child.'

'Prinny is a bit long in the tooth to be considered a child,' the Marquis said.

'Amanda!' Roxanne was immediately recalled to her duties as chaperon. 'Pray, don't lean over the box in that way. We can't have people stigmatising us as dowds.'

'They wouldn't do any such thing!'

'You'd be surprised about what they would do,' Roxanne chided.

Amanda sat back in her chair. 'If we were countrified dowds, the Marquis would not have asked us here,' she pointed out, and scored a hit as both Roxanne and the Marquis laughed. But in another moment she had found something of more interest. 'Lord Stanwyck, pray, who is that woman dressed all in gold?'

The Marquis gazed equably down at the woman in question, who was none other than Mrs Kinney, accompanied tonight by Webbe.

'That is Mrs Kinney, and no, minx, I shan't introduce you.'

'How did you know I was going to ask that? And anyway I knew you'd say no. Who is the gentleman with her?'

'Viscount Webbe,' Stanwyck said, thinking that Fanny had obviously crossed her Rubicon.

'Now, Amanda, do stop hounding Lord Stanwyck,' Roxanne said, beset herself with the liveliest curiosity about the Marquis's *chère amie* and her new gentleman. Could it be possible that anyone would throw over the Marquis?

She found no answer to that question in the bland expression on the Marquis's face, nor in that of the raven-haired Fanny down below. Within minutes, however, the curtain rose, and all thoughts of the Marquis's romantic entanglements vanished as she was transfixed by the unfolding action.

The performance was not in the strictest sense a play. Rather the evening featured a number of skits, songs and dances, and a re-enactment of a scene from *Troilus and Cressida* which even Amanda, who had no love of history, was obliged to applaud.

'I thought I could sing and dance well enough,' she said, after the performance was over. 'But I'm not so certain now.' She looked forlorn.

'Cheer up, lass,' Stanwyck said, hoping that this might dissuade her from joining the next travelling theatre, 'You can learn. You're still young.'

'Yes,' she agreed. 'And I can also play the harp and the pianoforte.'

The Marquis murmured an appreciative sound at these skills as he led them down the crowded stairs.

'Nigel Elcot, as I live and breathe!' a voice exclaimed as they came to the door.

'Laura, what are you doing here?' Stanwyck asked, stopping in front of a red-haired lady.

'Getting some inspiration of course, my dear!' she said, pecking him on the cheek.

'Laura, allow me to introduce two friends, Miss Roxanne Franklin and Miss Amanda Franklin. This is Lady Laura Carlisle, who has the misfortune to have a connexion to me.'

Laura trilled with laughter and shook hands with Roxanne and Amanda. 'Would you be any relation to General Franklin?'

'He is our grandfather,' Roxanne acknowledged.

'You poor dears!' Lady Laura was all sympathy. 'A stiff-necked martinet is what my brother Ben used to call him. And he should know, for I believe he served under him.'

'How is Benjamin?' Stanwyck asked.

'None the worse for receiving that ball in the shoulder,' Laura said cheerfully. 'Of course he's as sulky as a bear since the French are now defeated. In the beginning the wound was a novelty, and females would fuss over him. Now he finds their pity has worn thin. He'd much rather be out hunting and boxing and all the other odious things gentlemen do to pass their time.'

'What a ringing indictment of my sex,' Stanwyck said. 'I suppose you are much better than Ben? Dashing off to your portrait-painter and running those amateur theatricals. And are you still the inspiration of that poet?'

Lady Laura gurgled with laughter. 'No, and such a relief. I vow he was beginning to bore me with all those sonnets about my eyes and hair. I felt that if I tried a new hairstyle he would be forced into writing about it. But enough about me. What brought you to Drury Lane tonight?'

'Amanda,' Stanwyck said. 'She is an enthusiast like you.'

'Are you fond of the theatre, child?' Lady Laura asked, recognising a kindred spirit.

'Oh, ma'am. Have you heard of the Italian Players?'

'Of course! Their name is legion.'

'Well, Signor Fernando, their leader, was quite impressed by my abilities. I would have joined his troupe, but Roxanne here did not think my grandfather would approve. I was tempted to join the troupe anyway!'

'Amanda!' Roxanne said, stricken.

Such confessions might have shocked another lady of Quality, but Lady Laura herself, as she cheerfully revealed now, had once tried to run off and join a gipsy caravan. Fortunately, she was recalled to her senses by the time she reached the bottom of the stairs of her father's house.

'If you are interested in the theatre, child, you must take part in my amateur theatricals. Rehearsals are under way now. Come along tomorrow, and we'll see what role you are right for. You too, Miss Franklin.' She smiled at Roxanne. 'Nigel can give you directions, or—better yet—he can bring you himself.'

CHAPTER FIVE

THE MARQUIS, however, turned cat in the pan at the notion of attending any rehearsal at Laura's, and it fell to Roxanne to bear Amanda company the following day. Roxanne had learned from him that Lady Laura had been widowed at twenty-two and had spent the decade that followed laughing off any other proposals of marriage, devoting herself instead to her theatricals.

Her Cavendish Square residence certainly bustled with noise and excitement as they entered. Amanda was swiftly taken aside, introduced to several agreeable young ladies and was happily embroiled in a vigorous rehearsal of *A Midsummer Night's Dream*.

'And as for you'—Laura turned to Roxanne—'I would like you to meet my brother.' She led the way towards the crimson saloon. 'Pay no heed to him if he should be churlish. It comes from his injury.'

Roxanne nodded her understanding. 'I nursed my father before his death. He was sometimes ill-tempered. But when he was healthy, he was the sweetest man alive.'

'Well, no one can claim Benjamin is that, even when enjoying robust good health,' Laura warned as they came to the drawing-room.

The young man reclining on an Egyptian couch looked up at once as they entered. Red-haired like his sister, he sported a full beard and a purple sling about one arm. A litter of journals, a scattering of chess-men and several discarded novels on the Wilton carpet testified to his attempts to amuse himself.

'Benjamin, I should like you to meet Miss Franklin, a friend of Stanwyck's. Miss Franklin, my brother, Major Benjamin Bentley, who does not always sit like a bump on a log, I assure you.'

'Unfair, Laura,' he protested, rising to his feet and smiling down at Roxanne. 'I'm pleased to make your acquaintance, Miss Franklin.'

His eyes were a merry blue. And the shaggy beard reminded her of a pup she once owned.

'I must return to the rehearsal, but I'll leave you two to become better acquainted,' Laura said, drifting away.

A bit surprised at being deserted, Roxanne shot an uncertain glance at her hostess's retreating back.

Ben grinned. 'Sit down, Miss Franklin. I promise I shan't eat you.'

'I hope not,' she answered, laughing as she cleared the Windsor chair of several copies of the *Gentleman's Monthly*. 'You are a prodigious reader,' she said, seating herself.

'It only appears like that. I own to being partial to the *Gentleman's Monthly*. I've been trying to decide what colour cravat I ought to wear to Lady Tottingham's ball next Friday. What are your thoughts on the matter? Do you think green would be too daring?'

Roxanne swallowed hard. 'Did you say *green*, sir?'

The major nodded.

'Well, actually, I know very little about the intricacies of a male wardrobe,' she confessed, 'but I've always considered a white cravat suitable for all occasions.'

He looked crestfallen. 'That's what Laura tells me. But white strikes me as displaying such a sad want of dash.'

'Perhaps so,' Roxanne agreed. 'As I said before, I know little of such matters. But Stanwyck is acknowledged to be quite a Brummell. Why don't you put the question to him?'

Ben grimaced. 'If I did, he'd laugh so hard there would be no bearing it. And I dare say that gives me the answer to my question. I suppose it shall have to be the white cravat.' That matter settled, he turned to another. 'Are you a good friend of Nigel's?'

She gave her head a vehement shake, unwilling to claim friendship where there was mere acquaintanceship. 'Actually he was kind enough to call me a friend last evening when he introduced me to your sister, but our meeting is very recent. Hardly a friendship at all.'

'What a shame. I was hoping you would put in a good word for me concerning my membership in the Four Horse Club. Stanwyck won't enter my name, or Andrew's either, more's the pity. Andrew's his nephew,' he explained, seeing the foggy look on Roxanne's face. 'And he's the best of good fellows.'

'Why won't the Marquis put you up for membership?'

'He thinks I'm deuced cowhanded,' Benjamin answered. 'I don't know what flaw he finds in Andrew. And he could be right about my handling the reins,' he admitted ruefully. 'But at least I'm not such a gudgeon as to lose a hunting-box at cards in the way Andrew did. Do you play?'

Roxanne, following the tortuous turns of the major's conversation, deduced that an invitation to play cards had been tendered.

'A little,' she said now.

'Good.' He seemed pleased. 'Why don't we play, then? Just for fun, of course.' His merry grin flashed again, and she found herself responding to it with a grin of her own. 'I don't mind telling you that I don't have a feather to fly with. But things are devilishly dull here. The only other diversion under this roof is theatrics, and I've never been interested in the stage.' He walked over to the mantelpiece as he spoke. Opening a box, he extracted a pack of cards. 'Now, Miss Franklin, what is your pleasure?'

Now that the opportunity had arisen, Roxanne confessed to a lifelong curiosity about faro.

'Wonder no more, dear lady,' Ben said. 'Your first lesson is about to commence.'

The Major was as good as his word, and he proved to be an excellent teacher, encouraging her and laughing good-naturedly at the inevitable mistakes that occurred. By the end of an hour Roxanne had not only a grasp of the fundamentals of faro, but also of whist and hazard, a box of dice having been resurrected from a nearby desk.

'You are a splendid student,' Ben complimented, 'but just the same, don't fall in with the Captain Sharps.'

'I shan't,' she assured him. 'I have no intention of losing a fortune I don't possess. But you seem proficient in cards, Major.'

'Well, I'm male, after all,' he pointed out unnecessarily. 'And we must acquit ourselves at cards to one degree or another. But if you wish to see a master at work, you should catch Stanwyck in action at White's.'

'A privilege denied to me, since females are barred from those premises,' she reminded him.

'So they are,' Ben said, much struck. His face cleared after a second. 'But they ain't barred from the cardrooms of Almack's. We'll see you there, surely?'

Roxanne shook her head. Almack's Assembly Rooms were a far cry from the quiet house in Curzon Street.

'Actually, Amanda and I live very quietly by ourselves,' she said. 'We don't propose to attend balls and the routs of the Season.' She did not add that they had no expectation of being invited to any of these parties.

'And why not?' Ben demanded. 'Are you Quakerish? No, that can't be,' he corrected himself at once. 'You've been playing cards with me for the last hour. And you're no cit or mushroom, I can tell. Surely you didn't come to London to be a hermit? It would do you a world of good to attend a ball or two.'

'From what Lady Laura divulged, you were a trifle bored with Society yourself, Major. How is it you sing its praises now?'

The old grin flashed. '*Touché*, Miss Franklin. But do listen to me. I grant you your dislike of ton ways. I share some of them, in fact. But how much have you seen of London itself?'

'We've been to the Park and seen Carlton House, of course.'

Ben clucked his tongue. 'You've seen nothing of the city! How would it sit if I served as your guide?'

Ben was such a persuasive young gentleman that Roxanne could not have declined such a proposition if she had wanted to. Knowing he was undoubtedly bored with his injury, she fell in happily with the scheme that promised to afford them both amusement, and they made plans to begin the next afternoon with a tour of St Paul's. It had to be the afternoon, Ben explained apologetically, because his morning was claimed by an auction at Tattersall's.

While Roxanne was pursuing her acquaintance with Ben, the Marquis stood in the midst of Mr Weston's shop enduring the tedium of being measured and fitted with one of that paragon's justly famous waistcoats. He had just finished approving the three new orders, when the door to the shop opened and an irate Andrew Finch-William stalked in.

'So here you are, Uncle Nigel! Thank you so much for nothing,' he said with icy courtesy.

Stanwyck was considerably taken aback. Andrew was an amiable fellow as a rule. What had happened to set him off?

'My dear boy, you look all put about. Pray, what has happened?'

'I am not *your* dear boy.' The younger man spoke through gritted teeth. 'And you know what has happened. I should have suspected that you would go straight off to Father on the matter of the hunting-box. Probably you couldn't wait to carry the tale home. Well, I hope you're satisfied. He's redeemed it for twice its worth from that cur Webbe, and I am being sent to Haveril.'

'When did all this happen?' the Marquis asked curtly.

'Not an hour ago! So thank you so much, Uncle Nigel, for keeping your word to me.' With sarcasm dripping from his tongue, Andrew departed as quickly as he had descended.

As appropriate to one serving the Quality, Weston did not appear to have noticed anything untoward. He continued to pin and tuck. Not so the Marquis, whose mind whirled like a Catherine-wheel.

Webbe had evidently sold the hunting-box to Thaddeus. But why? He had only to contact him, and the matter would have been fully resolved. It seemed, Stanwyck thought grimly, as though Webbe had gone out of his way to stir up mischief.

Quitting Weston's shop, the Marquis drove his high-perch phaeton to his brother-in-law's residence in Mount Street, determined to get to the root of the matter.

He found Lord Haverly just about to partake of a hearty noon meal.

'Have something, Nigel,' he invited him.

The Marquis acquiesced in a small helping of smelts and boiled eels.

'Try the pineapple,' Lord Haverly suggested. 'Sweet as ambrosia. What did you think of the match between Black Bart and the Italian? Bit of a disappointment to me. I thought the match would last at least an hour. Wasn't half that.'

'It was quick,' Stanwyck agreed, slicing into the pineapple and finding it as sweet as promised. 'But it was best to put the man out of his misery.'

'Easy for you to say,' Lord Haverly grunted. 'I was backing the Italian.'

The Marquis made a sympathetic sound. 'I met Andrew today in Weston's,' he said, introducing the topic of interest to him. 'He mentioned being sent to Haveril.'

'Ay,' Lord Haverly said, wiping both ends of his moustache with a napkin. 'And don't bother to plead his cause. My mind is made up.'

'I don't intend to plead anything,' Stanwyck said mildly. 'But it seems a drastic measure for the middle of the Season.'

A look of annoyance crossed Haverly's cherubic cheeks. 'Devil take it, Stanwyck, it's not as though I like doing this! I know the lad will miss the balls and routs. But this is a serious matter. He lost the hunting-box his uncle Elcot left him. It fell into Webbe's hands somehow, and the vulture demanded twice its worth from me.'

He had come to the point in his narrative which intrigued Stanwyck.

'And you gave it to him?'

Haverly looked astonished. 'I had to,' he said, reapplying himself after another moment to another piece of pineapple. 'What would Gwen say if she returned and discovered it? Her side of the family, and all. That aunt of hers is a regular Tartar, you know that. She's your aunt, too.'

'But must you send Andrew away, Thaddeus?' Nigel asked, sidestepping the Tartar that was his Aunt Gertrude.

Lord Haverly put down his fork. 'Yes! I know he's prone to larks, and that don't bother me as a rule. But a sojourn in the country will give him something besides larks to dream up. I don't want him turning into one of those Bond Street beaux we see every day, full of stuff and no substance.'

Stanwyck rejected such a notion. 'He's too much your son for such a foolish thing to occur.'

Lord Haverly looked gratified, but he gave his head a doubtful shake. 'One never knows. Early days yet with Andrew. I shan't have my son turning into a flibberti-gibbet. Just look at young Ted Lucas. Ran off with a ballerina, leaving behind his wife and two babes.'

'Andrew doesn't have a wife,' Nigel pointed out meticulously, 'or even one babe!'

'Not yet, thank God,' Lord Haverly said grimly. 'Then there's McFarland. Met his people the other day. His mother was close to distraction because he has taken the notion of becoming an artist, talking fustian about his Muse, turned into a painter or poet or some such. Hard to understand her amid the vapours. But I'll be dashed if Andrew turns into one of those. And anyway, a little country air shan't kill him.'

The Marquis was inclined to agree. 'How did you find out about Webbe and the hunting-box?'

'Webbe sent me a message. I think him a bit of a jack-anapes, although the females dote on him so. But at least the hunting-box is back in the family.'

'You forget that Andrew is very angry.'

Haverly grunted. 'Livid! Called me an antiquated old fusspot. And had some unkind words to say about you as well.' He stared curiously across the table. 'He seemed to blame you for something. Wouldn't say why precisely.'

The Marquis did not choose to enlighten him.

'At any rate we fossils can rest our bones,' Haverly went on. 'Have you any word from Jonathon? Where is he this month—the Indies?'

'I believe so. But he is such a poor correspondent, which is to the good, for he has the muddiest hand in the kingdom. It gives me a headache to decipher a letter of his. He's supposed to be back in London any time this spring. But then it would be like him to change his mind and head for China.'

'Not China,' Lord Haverly protested with some vigour. 'Queer nab, that Jonathon. I know he's your heir and all, but he strikes me as peculiar, so set on travelling. I went to the Continent once, and that was more than enough. Had to put up at old inns, the most primitive of lodgings. You can keep it.'

'Oh, I agree with you wholeheartedly,' Stanwyck said with a laugh. 'I am sorely addicted to my creature comforts.'

'Speaking of which'—his brother-in-law gave him a meaningful look—'I saw Mrs Kinney in the company of Webbe the other day.'

'So did I. She seems to have made a new conquest.'

Haverly met his eye. 'Finished, Nigel?'

Stanwyck smiled. 'Finished, Thaddeus.'

'She wasn't your style,' Lord Haverly said, then, fearing that he had overstepped himself, hastily turned the topic. 'Are you going to the auction tomorrow? Prime Arabian is on the block. It's bound to cost a pretty penny.'

'I've seen the animal,' Stanwyck acknowledged. 'And I hope to leave Tattersall's with it in hand.'

'Do you, by Jove?' Lord Haverly's moustache twitched with excitement. 'I've heard those same words from at least half a dozen others. The bidding will be steep.'

'Without a doubt. I'll see you there, Thaddeus,' he said and took his leave.

Not only were the Marquis and his brother-in-law in attendance the next morning at Tattersall's, but practically all the gentlemen currently residing in London. Each of the sporting mad was determined to buy the steed for himself, while the dandies were assured of a good spectacle just by being at the auction.

The Arabian was the best of the lot on the block that morning, and he was not brought out until a dozen others had fallen under the gavel. The Marquis bore the wait cheerfully, but not so some of the others in the crowd, who began to shift restlessly and call for the Arabian.

When the animal was finally led into the ring, a hush approaching reverence fell on the onlookers. The steed was magnificent. The Marquis had examined the animal at length earlier in the week and did not have to glance at it again to know the coat was highly glossed, its teeth excellent, its legs long and strong, the colour jet black except for a spot of white on its right foreleg. Other buyers present might search for flaws, but such an effort, Stanwyck knew, was futile. The animal had no flaws. The only question that might have been raised against it was its spirit, which it was displaying now, shying and kicking its handlers. That was enough to cause a few who had earlier boasted of making the horse theirs change their minds. But it did not scare off Stanwyck.

Spirit was something he approved of in a mount, and he was quite ready to bid as high as necessary in order to win it.

'Nice-looking creature,' Lord Haverly murmured in his ear. 'Still set on it?'

The Marquis nodded. 'I've been looking for the right mount since Ajax broke his leg last month in a spill.'

The auctioneer, well aware of the prize before him, took ten minutes to detail the Arabian's magnificent features, then he started the bidding at a thousand pounds. A collective gasp swept the room. A thousand pounds? For a second it looked as though the auctioneer had miscalculated the opening bid, but Stanwyck gave a short nod. The auctioneer flashed him a grateful smile.

'We have a bid of a thousand pounds. One thousand. Do I hear one thousand one hundred? I do? Well, my lords'—he rubbed his hands together—'we are under way. One thousand two hundred pounds from the gentleman at the back. Prime Arabian horseflesh, gentlemen. One thousand three hundred, yes?'

Stanwyck nodded. The bidding was brisk, and after five minutes the bid stood at four thousand pounds. Lord Haverly fanned his two chins. The level of noise in the room alternated between cacophony and a hush as one after another the bidders dropped out. Finally only two were left: Stanwyck and Webbe.

'Four thousand one hundred?' The auctioneer looked at Webbe.

The Viscount nodded, a serene smile on his face. The Marquis felt a flicker of annoyance. He had a bone to pick with Webbe on the matter of young Andrew's hunting-box.

'Four thousand three hundred,' Stanwyck bid.

'Four thousand four?'

'Four thousand five.'

'Five thousand.' The Viscount's voice rang clear as a bell across the crowded area.

Stanwyck paused. The auctioneer, who had allowed the two temporarily to usurp his role, stepped deftly in.

'The last bid was five thousand, Lord Stanwyck.'

'Five thousand two hundred,' the Marquis countered.

'Five thousand five hundred,' Webbe replied.

'He's barmy!' A voice from the dandy set could be heard in the ensuing hush.

Webbe looked flushed with excitement, but not so the Marquis, who might have been purchasing a new pair of shoes.

'Six thousand,' he said quietly. He would be blue-devilled before he lost the Arabian to Webbe.

The Viscount could be seen inhaling a pinch of that foul-smelling snuff. 'Six thousand five,' he said finally.

'Seven thousand.'

The auctioneer wiped beads of perspiration from his brow. Webbe sent Stanwyck a fleeting smile from across the room, acknowledging his rival for the first time.

'Seven thousand five hundred.'

They were driving the price up far higher than anyone could have dreamed. Benjamin, standing in the rear of the crowd, felt a trifle giddy at the notion of anyone actually riding on a horse that cost so much.

'Eight thousand,' Stanwyck said.

'Eight thousand five hundred.'

'Nine thousand.'

'Nine thousand five.'

'Ten thousand.'

'Great Jupiter!' someone exclaimed.

'Eleven thousand,' Webbe countered.

Stanwyck stared at the Viscount. His eyes burned brightly at him. Did he wish to win the Arabian so badly? Eleven thousand for a horse which might command an acceptable high of four? He gave his head a rueful shake as though to clear it. His annoyance with the Viscount had very nearly caused him to miscalculate. He was interested in buying himself a horse, not in driving up the prices of horseflesh for everyone else in the ton.

'Viscount Webbe's last bid is eleven thousand, Lord Stanwyck,' the auctioneer said.

Stanwyck shook his head.

'Eleven thousand, going once, going twice, going three times. Gone. Sold to Viscount Webbe.'

A collective roar drowned out his words as the Viscount accepted the accolades of those around him.

'Pity,' Lord Haverly whispered consolingly into Stanwyck's ear. 'I knew you wanted it, Nigel.'

He led the way out, overhearing the remarks about how Webbe had finally bested Stanwyck, wondering if Nigel had heard, but his brother-in-law's expression was as composed as ever.

CHAPTER SIX

THE QUIZZES buzzed of nothing but the auction in the hours that followed. Even Roxanne, no student of horses, was obliged to listen to the full particulars of the bidding, by courtesy of Benjamin. The Major had presented himself as promised at Curzon Street that same afternoon for their whirlwind tour of London, which was capped by a breathless climb up to the Whispering Gallery of St Paul's. Benjamin's remarks about Mr Wren's genius were intermeshed with a few judicious comments about the rivalry some saw brewing between Webbe and Stanwyck.

As befitted an intimate of Mr Andrew Finch-William, Benjamin was not too pleased at the Marquis's turning tittle-tattle to Lord Haverly, but all the same he had hoped that Stanwyck would eventually triumph in the bidding for the Arabian.

'I don't think Webbe will lose an instant in riding the horse in the Park,' he told Roxanne now as they completed their descent from the gallery.

'Eleven thousand pounds,' Roxanne murmured, slightly winded from her climb. She could not comprehend such a sum. 'How extraordinary!'

'It's too dear for my blood,' Benjamin agreed as they settled into his carriage for the ride back to Curzon Street, where they found Stanwyck just about to step away from the door. He waited as they climbed down from the carriage.

'Good day, Miss Franklin.'

'Good day, Lord Stanwyck. What a surprise!' she said, then immediately took herself to task for such an inane greeting.

'A pleasant surprise, I dare hope?' he said with a smile. 'Hallo, Benjamin.'

'Stanwyck.'

'Have you been waiting long?' Roxanne asked the Marquis.

'I just arrived,' he assured her. 'Your butler explained that you were on an expedition with Ben here.'

'Seeing the sights,' she told him. 'Everything from the Tower to St Paul's. But why do we stand here gibble-gabbling? Come inside, and we shall have some tea. You'll join us, Ben, I hope?' she asked, turning to the Major.

Benjamin, however, declined, saying that he had promised his sister to carry out a round of errands.

'Where is Amanda?' the Marquis asked, after the Major had departed and they had gone into the parlour. 'Not taking in the sights with you?'

'Amanda is in the throes of rehearsal,' Roxanne explained, settling in front of a tray of tea-things. 'Surely you know the performance is slated for this week? She was able to procure a part because of Miss Fitzgibbons's twisting an ankle. Nothing could be more fortunate, I think you will agree? Not,' she said hastily, 'that one would wish a twisted ankle on anyone.'

'I comprehend your meaning,' he said. 'When is the play to be performed?'

'Thursday evening at Lady Laura's. Surely your invitation must have arrived? Lady Laura assured me she had despatched them herself.'

'I suppose so,' Stanwyck replied, sipping the tea. 'However, my secretary, being the diligent fellow he is, undoubtedly failed to bring it to my attention.'

'But you are coming, aren't you?' Roxanne said. 'You must.'

He cocked his head at her slightly. 'Why must I, ma'am?'

She coloured a little. Had she sounded too forward?

'I didn't mean to sound like a shrew,' she said at once. 'It's just that Amanda has been rehearsing her heart out. You know the performance will be of Mr Shakespeare's *A Midsummer Night's Dream*,' she said, handing him a tray of biscuits. 'Amanda plays the artisan, Bottom.'

'Good heavens!' Nigel ejaculated. 'That's the one with the ass's head.'

'Yes,' she said, choking on a laugh. 'It's quite a prime part. And she's been practising so hard with the head, and now no longer trips or walks into things, which is a great relief, for her knees were getting quite scraped!'

He laughed with her.

'She is looked forward to seeing you there.'

He held up a hand. 'Very well, Miss Franklin. I'll attend the performance if only to see Amanda with the ass's head!'

She gave a happy smile. 'I'm glad. Amanda shall be pleased.'

He sipped his tea again. 'Do you think it the duty of everyone to make those about them happy, Miss Franklin?'

His question surprised her, and she could not help wondering if he were vexed. 'No,' she said finally, having weighed the matter momentarily in her mind. 'But when it is such a trifle to make a friend happy, why shouldn't one do it? But I dare say you have a reason for calling here today, and I beg your pardon for having my tongue go on wheels!'

'I enjoyed it,' he told her. 'And yes, actually I do have a reason for my call. I had the opportunity to speak with Lord Bisbane. His wife is due to deliver her first child at any time this month and has need of a companion to assist her after the babe is born. Not a nurse,' he said quickly in answer to the question in her eyes. 'I know you acquitted yourself ably in that capacity to your father, and I doubt that you would wish to take on that role again. Lord Bisbane has already engaged a nurse to help with the babe. Rather, he'd like you to act as a companion to Lady Bisbane in the hectic weeks after the birth. Hold her hand, and well, I don't know precisely, but just tell her how splendidly she is doing.'

'That sounds easy enough,' Roxanne said. After the other situations she had considered, being a companion to Lady Bisbane sounded like a good offer indeed.

'I told her you would call,' the Marquis said, taking one of his cards from a gold case. He scrawled a few words on its back. 'Give this to her when you do visit.'

'Thank you, I shall,' she assured him, conscious of the favour he was bestowing. Why was he being so kind to her and Amanda?

'Has Mr Cartier returned here?' Stanwyck asked, breaking into her reverie.

'No,' she said. 'I sent him word of my refusal after you told me about his habits.'

'That's a relief. I shouldn't like to worry about you being in his clutches.'

'I don't see why you worry about me at all,' she said frankly. 'You have been good to concern yourself with my affairs, especially today when I know you must not have been in the best of humours.'

An odd glint flashed in his blue eyes.

'I heard about the auction,' she said simply.

He heaved a sigh. 'Friend Benjamin, I suppose?'

'Yes, but pray don't scold him. He couldn't but tell me about it, or he'd have burst! And I'm sorry you lost the bidding. Ben says you were very anxious to purchase the Arabian.'

'I was,' Stanwyck agreed. 'But I don't repine.'

'Still, it must have been a disappointment.'

He shrugged, and his shoulders moved lightly under his coat. 'One does not reach my ripe old age, Miss Franklin, without suffering some measure of disappointment in life; a few far more telling than the mere loss of a horse!'

Roxanne fell silent, realising that without a doubt he referred to his long-lost love, Miss Drusilla Crosby. That disappointment must surely have rankled more than a mere horse.

His purpose for the call accomplished, Stanwyck concluded his visit a few moments later and returned to his residence. As he strolled in the hall, he saw his hard-working secretary, Mr Stevens, hunched over a mound of bills and vouchers owed to the tradesmen. Remembering Roxanne's words about Amanda's début on stage, he stepped into his office to enquire whether an invitation to Lady Laura's theatricals had yet arrived.

'It came this morning,' Mr Stevens assured him. He was a few years younger than the Marquis, spare of frame, and still very much a clergyman's son—with a sense of propriety that Stanwyck delighted in testing. 'I was about to send your regrets.'

'Don't,' the Marquis ordered. 'I have decided to attend.'

Mr Stevens's jaw dropped. During the year and a half he had worked for the Marquis, he had never known his employer to attend any amateur theatrical in anyone's drawing-room. In fact, he distinctly recalled his lordship's stigmatising such events as gatherings for henwits.

Stanwyck laughed at the stupefaction on his secretary's face. 'Don't worry, Stevens, I have not gone queer in the attic. I promised to please someone by attending Laura's theatrical.'

Try as he might, Mr Stevens could not prevent an even more baffled expression from appearing on his countenance. The notion of the Marquis attempting to please anyone! But he was too well trained to do anything but murmur, 'Very good, sir.'

'By the way, Arthur, I didn't win the horse.'

Mr Stevens nodded, almost absently. The word of the auction had reached the household earlier in the day through an underfootman who had taken it upon himself to wait outside Tattersall's for the results.

'I heard, sir.'

Inwardly the Marquis cursed the prattle-boxes. They had had a busy day if both Miss Franklin and his staid secretary knew of his fate in less than two hours! 'I still have need of a mount.'

'Sir, I recollect my uncle's mentioning to me some months ago that Lord Julian Smythe of Derbyshire was having a run of bad luck at the tables.'

'What has that to do with my needing a mount?' Stanwyck asked impatiently.

'Today I ran into Edward Hancock. He used to be Lord Julian's secretary.'

'Used to be?' the Marquis quizzed.

Mr Stevens nodded. 'He told me he had been dismissed. With great regret, of course, but Lord Julian was forced to let him go. He could no longer pay him. He was being forced to sell off his possessions to pay off his creditors.'

'Lord Julian Smythe.' Stanwyck touched the tips of his fingers lightly together, trying to think why the name should tease his memory so. 'Wasn't he the one who had a notion to raise Arabians here?'

'Yes, sir.' Mr Stevens nodded. 'And from what Edward divulged, Lord Julian did have some capital bloodstock.'

'Did he now?' The Marquis clapped his secretary on the shoulder. 'Good work, Arthur. Perhaps I shall ride to Derbyshire tomorrow and look in on Lord Julian.' He was about to quit the office when Mr Stevens broached another matter.

'There is something that I have been meaning to call to your attention, sir.' He gave a discreet cough, which Stanwyck instantly recognised. Arthur was always rendered mildly inarticulate when it came to his muslin dealings.

Repressing a smile, the Marquis looked quizzically at the faint blush that stained Mr Stevens's downy cheeks.

'It's the lease to Mrs Kinney's house,' his secretary said at last, extending a document to him. 'It will be up in two weeks, if you notice. Shall I renew it as usual?'

'No. Allow the lease to expire,' the Marquis said.

His reply was not what his secretary expected. Mr Stevens looked up in shock. 'Allow the lease to expire?' he echoed.

Stanwyck nodded. 'But don't fall into a pelter, Arthur. Mrs Kinney will not be homeless for long. I dare say she'll find another roof over her head faster than you could utter the words high flyer.'

He sauntered off, thinking involuntarily of Fanny. It was a pity she had become so avaricious. Her beauty was unmistakable, as was her spirit. But she had become so demanding that after a time his enjoyment had palled.

The auction and tea with Miss Franklin had caused Stanwyck to neglect his usual visit to Manton's, and he remedied this with a late afternoon visit. As soon as he stepped into that establishment, however, he felt a coolness in the atmosphere. The silence persisted as he made his way towards his favourite position and target, and he intercepted several amused looks and pitying comments.

With the skill of an expert, he loaded his pistol and began to shoot, but his concentration was poor. After only half an hour—he usually spent twice that amount of time—he departed, his ears burning as he overheard the whispers linking his name with Webbe's.

Damn Webbe, anyway! With his colour high, he walked over to White's, wondering if he should have bid higher and won the Arabian if only to save himself from the quizzes.

After a light dinner at the club, Stanwyck's mood turned more benevolent, and he fell in comfortably with a suggestion of whist with Sir Bertram Sykes, Lord Grimsley and Mr Kirkpatrick. Relaxed, the Marquis played to enjoy himself, and won several hands. In this comfortable fashion the hours passed, only to be broken by the early departure of Mr Kirkpatrick. Quite excusable, all in all, since he was practically a newly-wed.

No sooner had Mr Kirkpatrick vacated his place than a replacement strolled up to the remaining three at the table.

'I hope you don't mind, Stanwyck,' Webbe said, flashing a confident smile which was partly explained by his triumph at Tattersall's. At long last he had bested the precious Marquis at something! An ample supply of sherry drunk with his cronies had also added to his feeling of superiority.

'Mind? Why should I mind?' Stanwyck asked pleasantly. Lord Grimsley, after shooting a quick look at the others at the table, waved the Viscount to the empty chair.

The Marquis gazed at him with bland disinterest. 'You won a horse, Webbe, not a war.'

The other two men at the table guffawed appreciatively. Webbe flushed darkly. The play at the table resumed, but Stanwyck's luck had turned with Webbe's arrival. The mood at the table had changed as well. Before, it had been a pleasant, relaxed way to pass a few hours; now, Webbe had a cutting comment to offer with every hand that was dealt. Stanwyck could not abide another minute of such mockery, and, rose after half an hour to take his leave.

'Don't go, Nigel,' Sir Bertram implored in his foggy voice.

'You only tell me that because I am a prime pigeon for you,' Stanwyck countered with an easy laugh as he prepared to pay off his losses to the three. 'The game has lost its pleasure for me.'

'Pity your day has been such an unsatisfactory one,' Webbe said with a yawn. 'But we both knew the auction was bound to end badly for one of us.'

'Speak for yourself, Webbe,' Stanwyck replied coldly. 'I found the outcome satisfactory enough.'

Webbe snorted with laughter. And even Sir Bertram cocked his craggy head at Stanwyck in disbelief.

'That's coming it too strong,' Webbe told him. 'Do you take us for flats? You wanted the Arabian as badly as I!'

'Obviously not,' Stanwyck contradicted him as he picked up his ivory-handled cane, 'since you outbid me. And as I rethink the matter, I'm glad you bid eleven thousand pounds. It saved me the folly of paying ten thousand pounds for a horse worth at best only four thousand.'

The Viscount's smile froze.

'I am not half as brave as you, Webbe,' Stanwyck went on. 'You can endure the slings and arrows that might follow such a purchase. I could not.'

Confusion etched itself plainly on Webbe's brow. Obviously he did not know what Stanwyck meant, but he was not about to admit it.

Sir Bertram had no such qualms. 'Slings and arrows? What the devil do you mean by that, Stanwyck?'

The Marquis took a pinch of snuff, conscious that their conversation was being followed avidly by not only those present at his table, but everyone else in the card-room.

'Perhaps I can explain it this way. Sir Bertram, you own a pair of greys, do you not?'

A smile spread on the Baronet's face. 'Ay, and a pretty pair they are, if I say so myself.'

'I agree. Now what price did you pay for the two of them?'

The Baronet frowned with the effort of remembering. 'Five hundred pounds, or thereabouts.'

'A fair price, I think we all would agree. Now what if I told you that, were you to buy that same pair tomorrow, it would cost you twice what you paid?'

'Eh? Double the price? Preposterous!'

The Marquis turned to Lord Grimsley. 'And you, Lord Grimsley. You've had your eye on that bay, have you not? What if its price doubles within the week? What would you say to that?'

'But why should the price double?' Webbe demanded before Grimsley could speak.

'Because,' the Marquis said with meticulous courtesy, 'a certain gentleman is foolish enough to drive the prices up for everyone by his exorbitant bidding.'

'But surely no one can hold that against me,' Webbe said, looking about him for support in the card-room. He found nothing but grim faces staring back at him.

'Hope you're wrong, Stanwyck.' Lord Grimsley glowered. 'I've been planning to buy that bay for a considerable time. One thousand pounds would be too deep for my purse.' He shot a baleful look at Webbe. The Marquis, observing that he had made his point, picked up his cane and sauntered away.

CHAPTER SEVEN

LADY BISBANE was pink-cheeked, curly-haired and very *enceinte*. She was also in awe of the bundle of joy she carried within her enormous belly, and equally in awe of her husband of two years and his acquaintance with the illustrious Marquis of Stanwyck.

'Edmund thinks that Stanwyck is the most complete hand,' she told Roxanne as they sat in her sitting-room. 'He's such a Corinthian, and yet not odiously starched up the way some are. When he suggested that a lady like yourself might be helpful to me, naturally we were inclined to agree.'

'That is kind of you,' Roxanne murmured.

Lady Bisbane batted her long eyelashes. Roxanne was reminded of a Dresden china doll. The young mother-to-be could be no more than eighteen herself.

'Not a servant, you must understand, or a nurse!' Lady Bisbane wrinkled up her chubby face. 'I have those. More like a friend, or so Edmund says. I vow I am in desperate need of company. Most of my friends are not even married!'

'It must all be a trifle daunting for you,' Roxanne said sympathetically.

'Yes. You do understand, don't you? It's not that I mind having the babe. I dare say nothing would complete our happiness more, and Edmund is partial to children. But all the same I can't help worrying.'

'I think we shall deal marvellously together,' Roxanne said, allaying any fears that Lady Bisbane might have

nursed. They came to a rapid agreement over the details
of her employment. She would move into the Green
Street residence as soon as Lady Bisbane had delivered—a period of perhaps a month from now. She
would stay on for at least a month and quite possibly
more.

That done, Roxanne left. She had only her intuition
to guide her, but she dearly hoped that Stanwyck had
not bullied the young couple too fiercely into engaging
her.

The next few days were busy ones for the Marquis.
First he journeyed to Derbyshire and found a suitable
replacement for his beloved Ajax in one of Lord Julian
Smythe's prime Arabians. The horse, Prince, was com-
pletely black and magnificent, boasting no discernible
flaws. Stanwyck managed to buy it for four thousand
pounds and made the arrangements for it to be brought
up to London later that week.

In a cheerful mood from his purchase, he next called
on his nephew in exile in the country and managed to
correct Andrew's mistaken notion that he had played
him false with Webbe. After winning Andrew over, he
stayed the night and then returned to London, feeling
in a mood of remarkable accomplishment. He had solved
the problem of finding a new mount, and his nephew
was no longer at outs with him. The only vexatious
problem left to tackle was Fanny.

After warning his groom, Albert, to expect the arrival
of Prince some time in the next week, the Marquis paid
a call on his *chère amie*. His visit occasioned her butler's
stammered apology and Fanny's emergence from her
boudoir flushed and still knotting a scarlet dressing-gown
about her waist.

'How now, Nigel, do you descend on me this way?' she demanded crossly.

'My apologies, Fanny. I didn't wish to be accused of neglecting you.'

'Neglect? You are jesting! But you time it poorly. I am waiting for a friend.'

'Waiting,' he quizzed, 'or entertaining one?' He pointed his Malacca cane at a cigar lying in one of the ashtrays on a pier table. 'Nasty habit, cigars. I've never smoked them myself. Don't bother to say a word, Fanny,' he said gently. 'The lease of this house is up in two weeks. I called in to tell you that I shan't be renewing it.'

'What?' For the first time since he had known her, anxiety showed on her face. 'But, Nigel, that's not fair!'

'Why don't you ask the gentleman with the cigars to renew it for you,' he suggested and was obliged to duck as she hurled the nearest object, the crystal ashtray, at his head.

The visit with Fanny left an unpleasant taste in the Marquis's mouth. She had been the last in a line of Cyprians to enjoy his favours in the years since Drusilla, and he would now have to begin the whole tedious sequence of finding a new mistress on whom to lavish the appropriate attention. Was it mere old age or indolence which made him fatigued at the very idea?

He drove away and stopped at the Berry Brothers in Bond Street to replenish his supply of snuff. He had just poked his nose into a jar of Macouba, when Philip Dudley hailed him.

'Nigel, why so pensive? Can choosing snuff be so much of a chore?'

'No, but taking leave of a ladybird can,' Stanwyck said.

'The lovely Fanny, I suppose?' his friend hazarded a guess. 'I suppose her last request for a trinket from Rundell's was the straw that broke the camel's back?'

Stanwyck put down the jar of Macouba. 'Camel? I vow I did sometimes feel like a beast of burden with her.'

'I could have told you she had an avaricious streak,' Philip said mildly. 'But you wouldn't have listened.'

'How would you know such a thing? I always thought you had a weakness for heiresses!'

Philip laughed, and the Marquis strolled over to dip a finger into a jar of Spanish Bran. It was a popular choice, but he preferred his mixture lightened with a pinch of Brazil.

'What you need, Nigel,' Philip said, following him about the shop, 'is a different sort of female.'

'Different?' the Marquis asked. 'Are they making them with two heads nowadays?'

'I mean a lady. A wife, if you will.'

The Marquis looked so stunned that Mr George Berry, standing behind the counter, reached quickly for the glass jar Stanwyck held in his hands.

'Good heavens, things aren't as desperate as that,' the Marquis scolded, as he allowed the proprietor to take away the jar.

'Do you have a successor to Fanny already in mind, then?'

Stanwyck sighed. 'No, but I dare say I'll find someone agreeable.'

'No doubt. She'll be pretty and younger than Fanny, but just as avaricious. How old are you, Stanwyck?'

The Marquis squirmed under this interrogation. 'What questions you ask! I'm a month older than you, as we both know.'

'Two-and-thirty. Of an age to be thinking of a wife,' Philip said, giving him a sidelong glance.

'You sound like my Great-aunt Gertrude,' Nigel said, handing him a sample of the snuff he was about to purchase.

Dudley took a pinch between thumb and forefinger, holding it up to one nostril. 'Very nice,' he exclaimed after a sniff. 'I'll have the same,' he told Mr Berry.

Their snuffboxes filled to the brim, the two gentlemen stepped out of the shop a few minutes later.

'Scored a pretty hit off Webbe last night, or so I understand,' Philip complimented him. 'I heard about it from more than one person.'

The Marquis smiled, relishing his small victory. It was only just that the Viscount should be the target of the quizzes now.

'I thought I'd give Webbe food for thought,' the Marquis said, a smile playing about his lips.

'Food? It was a veritable feast!' Philip scoffed. 'Word is, he's petrified at even showing himself on the Arabian. Your prophecy was on the mark, too. Grimsley says he had to pay far in excess of what the bay was worth. And other sellers are setting steeper prices as well. But I don't pity Webbe. If he suffers a snub, it's all he deserves. Since he came into the title, he has been lording it over some of us.'

Stanwyck stopped at his phaeton.

'Will I see you at White's tonight?' his friend enquired. 'Webbe probably won't show his face for fear of being quizzed by the others.'

The Marquis shook his head. 'Not till very late. I am promised earlier to Laura.'

'Laura? But . . .' Philip turned, thunderstruck. 'Nigel, you can't mean you're attending that theatrical of hers! You must be roasting me.'

'Not at all. Enjoy the snuff, Philip,' he said and climbed into his vehicle, leaving Mr Dudley still standing with a bemused expression on his face.

The long gallery of Lady Laura's residence in Cavendish Square had been transformed from a sedate, tasteful English room to the Athenian forest dictated by the constraints of Mr Shakespeare's play, a metamorphosis that had taxed the skills and patience of the entire household staff, leading to no less than three minor skirmishes between the servants and the performers. But all the work was deemed worth it when the night of the performance arrived.

'My word, Laura,' Mrs Connaught, a silver-haired lover of the fine arts, trilled a greeting as she entered the drawing-room and clasped her hostess to her broad bosom. 'This is too thrilling!' She took a step back and was nearly decapitated by the olive tree that represented the Athenian wood.

'Thank you, Millicent,' Laura said, looking lovely in a gown of seawater silk. 'Wait until you see the costumes and the setting. I vow it was worth all the work.'

She led her friend to a chair in the front row and then turned to greet her other guests. Stanwyck, entering, stood for a moment, transfixed by the scene in front of him. Then slowly he made his way in. Miss Franklin was not about, but he received an impudent grin and wave from Amanda. He only prayed that she would be able to balance her ass's head successfully.

'Does it meet with your approval, Nigel?' Laura came up to him as he surveyed the room with his quizzing-glass.

He put the glass down and shot her an incredulous look. 'Unfair, my dear. I am no critic. But everything seems quite in order, particularly you. With all that green you're wearing, one would almost take you for a wood nymph,' he teased.

'And one might take you for a Tulip,' she retorted, taking the sting out of her words by pecking him on the cheek, 'by that cravat you are wearing. Is it a new arrangement?'

'It's a new variation on an old arrangement,' he corrected gently. 'Where is brother Ben?'

'Showing Miss Franklin his library.'

The Marquis frowned. 'He seems to be spending much time in her company these days. Don't tell me he's dangling after her?'

Lady Laura was rocked. 'My word, no, Nigel. Ben is merely bored with his injury, and Roxanne has been civil enough to take an interest in him and coax him out of his gloom. They get on well together, but to speak of their entertaining *tendres*...' She hushed him abruptly. 'Here they come.' She directed a smile at her brother and Roxanne, who wore the same simple silk that she had worn to Drury Lane.

'Nigel is here, Ben.'

'So I see. Evening, Stanwyck. Ready for the forest of Arden?'

His sister sighed. 'That is *As You Like It*, you gudgeon! We are performing *A Midsummer Night's Dream*.'

'Well, it's one or the other,' Ben agreed happily. 'I don't see the need to cut up stiff over the difference.

Both comedies. Both have to do with love. Both written by Mr Shakespeare. Both taking place in forests of some kind.'

Lady Laura clucked her tongue. 'It's not the same at all! It's as though you were set to marry one female with blonde hair and blue eyes. You just wouldn't pick out another with blonde hair and blue eyes and say she would do just as well, would you?'

'No, by heaven!' Ben appeared appalled. 'You forget, I have a decided preference for brunettes!'

Lady Laura flung her hands heavenward and moved away.

'What was Ben showing you?' Stanwyck asked Roxanne.

'His collection of books.'

'I didn't know he had one,' the Marquis murmured.

'Of course I have a collection, Stanwyck,' Ben railed. 'It's not up to your standards.' He turned to Roxanne. 'You must get Nigel to show you his collection. I suspect that he actually reads some of them!' He turned his attention back to the Marquis, squinting suddenly. 'By Jove, that's a new neckcloth. What is it?'

'A variation on the Trône d'Amour,' he informed him.

Ben raised his quizzing-glass to his eye. 'Very pretty, I must say. And damn intricate, I'd wager.'

'It is,' the Marquis agreed, recalling the four linen cloths he had crushed in the process of fashioning the one about his neck now.

'I wish you'd teach it to me.'

'Perhaps, but not this evening. There is a performance to be seen.'

'Don't remind me!' Ben grimaced, and then, recalled to his duties as a reluctant host by a signal from his sister, went off to do the pretty to a set of dowagers.

'Is Amanda very nervous this evening?' Stanwyck asked as he and Roxanne found seats in the room.

Roxanne shook her head. 'No. It's quite surprising to me. I vow I would be in a quake. She seems quite the seasoned performer.'

'Yes, I know.' He grinned. 'She can sing and dance and die extremely well.'

'Well, she can!' Roxanne asserted with a laugh. 'And she has been rehearsing furiously. She knows all her lines and loves the ass's head she is to wear.'

Stanwyck was about to offer a comment on this last remark, but they were quickly hushed by others about them as several of the candles were dimmed and the performers began to move on to the makeshift stage.

A good two hours later, the Marquis, his bones creaking only a little, rose with the others to join in the applause. He had never been an admirer of Mr Shakespeare, but he had to admit the performance was creditable enough. He had enjoyed himself, an occurrence he supposed had something to do with his companion who had suffered through each of Amanda's appearances, breathing sighs of relief when the right words were spoken. Now relief and pride were evident on Roxanne's face.

'It was good, wasn't it?' she whispered to him.

He smiled down at her. 'It was,' he agreed, perjuring his soul without a qualm. They followed the crowd towards the performers and their hostess.

'First rate, Laura, first rate,' Stanwyck acclaimed when they found her.

Lady Laura beamed and looked gratified by his words. 'I did think it went off well,' she agreed. 'Everyone filled his part to perfection. I've been thinking whether we ought to hold another performance. Such a pity just to have one night of it, after working so hard. But some are determined to have another play instead. Ben, will you lead everyone to the refreshments?'

Thus summoned, Ben began to herd the guests towards the refreshment-room. Roxanne lingered behind with Stanwyck, hoping for a word with the triumphant Amanda still habited in her artisan's costume.

'Well, sir?' she asked impishly.

'You were the best Bottom I can recall seeing,' he said gallantly.

She flushed with pleasure and gave him an exuberant hug.

'Amanda!' Roxanne scolded.

'I can't help it, Cousin Roxanne,' Amanda said. 'I have the Marquis to thank for this night. It's beyond anything I've ever experienced. Performing, I mean. Look, there's Signor Fernando. You remember him, don't you?'

'I certainly do,' the Marquis said. 'What can he want?'

The leader of the Italian Players wanted nothing more than to congratulate the young signorina on her night of triumph.

'A performance worthy of a Siddons, my dear Miss Franklin.'

'That is nice of you to say.' Amanda blushed, all thoughts of her previous altercation with him ended.

'Indeed, you would be a worthy member of any troupe!'

'Cousin Roxanne, did you hear that? Didn't I tell you?'

'Yes, Amanda, and it's quite a compliment, but I'm afraid you're not going to tread the boards professionally.' She turned to Signor Fernando. 'My cousin is too young for that. And now, Amanda, I'm certain that Lady Laura would wish to congratulate you on your performance.'

'A very nice move,' the Marquis murmured approvingly to her as they moved towards the refreshment-room.

She grinned, but her smile froze as they entered the hall.

'What is it?' he demanded. She had turned ash white and looked ready to faint.

'It's my grandfather,' she murmured, as the general came through the doorway towards them, wearing a thundercloud expression on his doughty face.

CHAPTER EIGHT

THE GRIZZLED figure advancing across the black and white lozenges was a veteran of numerous battles with the French during the years at war with Napoleon, and he wore a visage so stern that it might well have quelled any uprising on the spot. It certainly put Roxanne into the liveliest fear.

She managed none the less to control herself and to welcome her grandfather with every show of pleasure.

'Good evening, Grandfather. What a delightful surprise to see you here.'

'Don't try and pitch that gammon to me!' the general barked. 'A nice piece of business you've stirred up! I went to Curzon Street, expecting to find you and your young cousin. Instead, I learn you are here at a theatrical!' His inflection left no doubt as to his opinion of Shakespeare and company.

'*A Midsummer Night's Dream*,' Roxanne felt moved to protest. 'By Mr Shakespeare. Quite legitimate.'

The general growled something incomprehensible, and his glare became even more pronounced when he spotted Amanda still attired in her artisan's costume.

'By Jove, what is that you have on?' he ejaculated as Amanda skipped up happily. 'Don't tell me it's trousers!'

'It's my costume, Grandfather,' Amanda replied.

The general's brows drew together. 'Costume? Do you mean you took part in this theatrical? By heaven, a grand-daughter of mine to put herself up to such scorn! Hoydenish doings!'

Roxanne blinked under this tide of emotion. 'It wasn't so scandalous, I assure you,' she said hastily. 'And Amanda performed quite well in her part.'

'She performed inexecrably!' the general said trenchantly. 'And you are entirely to blame. I gave you charge of her, but you appear to be as dull-witted as she. What shall I do with the pair of you?' he demanded of no one in particular. 'I could send her to a convent, I dare say...'

'A convent?' Amanda broke into her grandfather's tirade. 'Oh, not a convent, Grandfather,' she pleaded. 'I shall be good, I promise. Besides'—a hint of the old Amanda came to the surface—'I'll just run away from a convent.'

'Not this one,' the general retorted grimly. 'The walls are ten feet high. I've already had a word with the Mother Superior.'

'Amanda does not deserve punishment, Grandfather,' Roxanne put in quickly as Amanda burst into tears, a dramatic touch that left the general unmoved. 'I was responsible for her.'

'You,' the general said crushingly, 'are a mite old for a convent.'

Roxanne bit her tongue, conscious of her burning cheeks. Her grandfather need not have made her feel as old as Methuselah, particularly in front of the Marquis!

'Actually,' a quiet voice intervened in the family dispute, 'if you wish to point the finger of blame at anyone, sir, you'd best point it at me.'

Stanwyck's words, for it was he who had spoken, caused the general to switch his head in his direction. One glimpse at the exquisite gentleman facing him, and he snorted. 'You're to blame? And pray who might you be?' he asked with icy courtesy.

'Stanwyck.'

'He's a marquis, Grandfather,' Amanda said helpfully as the general searched his memory.

'A marquis?' General Franklin fixed a baleful eye on Stanwyck. 'I see what game you're running. But it won't work on any of my grand-daughters!'

'What the devil are you prattling about, Franklin?' the Marquis asked bracingly.

'It's plain as day what your game is,' the general said, looking grim. 'Unhappily for you, I'm here to queer it. You might have succeeded in pulling the wool over Roxanne's eyes, but I've seen your ilk before. Rich, lazy, a barley-straw, in fact!'

'Grandfather!' Roxanne protested. Her face was scarlet with mortification. She dared not stand idly by and let the Marquis be so besmirched. 'You misunderstand. Lord Stanwyck has been a great friend to us here in London. He's been such a help.'

'A great friend, is it?' the general scoffed. 'But at what cost to your reputation? Don't you see what's afoot, you stupid girl? He's out to find himself a new ladybird, encouraging her to the stage—which no self-respecting female would ever countenance!'

'No, Grandfather,' Amanda exclaimed, taking up the cudgels in Stanwyck's defence, 'you wrong him. And as for a ladybird, he has one of his own, far prettier than either Roxanne or me. And as for encouraging me to tread the boards, he claims he'd spank me if I did any such thing.'

'Hmph.'

'Amanda is right,' Roxanne asserted. 'The Marquis has been kind enough to lend us his support. I can't think how we would have managed without his assistance. And I shan't have you insulting him in this way.'

The general looked amazed. Was this the little Roxanne whom he had been so accustomed to ordering about? 'I shall insult whomever I please.'

'A trait excusable in one of your years,' the Marquis said.

The general cast a swift glance at Stanwyck. 'Do you wish to call me out?' he demanded.

A fleeting smile touched Stanwyck's lips. 'I never duel with anyone two decades older than myself,' he said politely.

'Bosh!' The general turned back to his granddaughters. 'You two ramshackle creatures are coming home with me now,' he announced, and strode to the door, taking for granted that they would follow. Amanda looked uncertainly at Roxanne for direction.

After a moment, Roxanne nodded, and they began to walk quietly towards the door.

'You will be all right?' Stanwyck asked in an undertone.

'Oh, yes.' She made a valiant smile. 'Grandfather is merely caught by surprise, and so is twitty. He'll calm down soon enough.'

This easy assurance did not entirely satisfy him, but Stanwyck had no choice but to let them pass out of his company with the general. But later, as he shared a lobster patty with Lady Laura, he decided to rise early and pay a visit at Curzon Street the next morning.

The atmosphere in the general's barouche could best be described as frigid. Having exhausted himself with his tirade at Cavendish Square, the general contented himself now with glowering at his grand-daughters, neither of whom was inclined towards conversation.

The carriage stopped at Curzon Street, and Roxanne and Amanda descended. The general had his quarters at Albemarle Street, and he leaned his head out of the carriage now to say he would call the next morning at ten to deal with them. Then he settled back in his seat and gave the order to depart.

'Well, I like that,' Amanda said, standing with her hands on her hips. 'We could have stayed at Lady Laura's, if that's all he wanted with us. I don't remember him being so odious before, do you?'

'Father used to call him an ill-tempered ogre,' Roxanne revealed. 'And I'm inclined to agree if he threatens you with a convent.'

'But he can't do that, can he?' Amanda asked as they went up the stairs.

'I'm afraid Grandfather can do pretty much what he wants,' Roxanne said.

Amanda drew an audible breath. 'Cousin Roxanne, what shall we do?'

'For the moment, we must get you out of these clothes,' Roxanne said by way of an answer. 'They give you a very odd appearance, so it's no wonder Grandfather took the wrong notion into his head.' She gave the order to Kate for a warm bath to be drawn.

'I shall die in a convent, I know it,' Amanda moaned.

'Try not to fall into a pelter,' Roxanne soothed. 'In the morning he will feel differently. Perhaps he'll just send you on a visit to Aunt Peg in York. She is amiable enough. And have I told you what a splendid Bottom you were tonight? You remembered all your lines. Quite clever! I should have forgotten half of them.'

With a little coaxing she managed to get Amanda to bed, promising that they would deal with the general tomorrow together. It was not so easy to coax herself to sleep that night. Long after the one o'clock hour had sounded, Roxanne lay awake in her room, wondering what the general's return meant for her and Amanda.

Finally she fell asleep. When she opened her eyes, sunlight was streaming through the curtains of the windows. Instantly she sat bolt upright. It was nearly nine o'clock, Jennie told her as she carried in the breakfast-tray.

After gulping down a cup of coffee, Roxanne went into Amanda's room, expecting to find her still in bed. Instead, the room was empty. Turning from the bed, Roxanne noticed a letter on the small bureau, and with an odd feeling of foreboding, she snatched it up.

> Cousin Roxanne,
> I can't live in a convent. I have gone. I shall be all right. Do not worry. Kate comes with me.
>
> > Love,
> > Amanda

'She's run off,' Roxanne whispered to herself. Quickly she left the room and intercepted Jennie on her way down the stairs with the breakfast-tray. She interrogated her swiftly about Kate's complicity in the runaway.

'Kate said nary a word to me, Miss Roxanne,' Jennie said. 'I thought she be mighty quiet last night. She went into Miss Amanda and had a long coze with her. But I thought they were just talking over the play, the way they like to do.'

'Don't blame yourself,' Roxanne soothed. 'But do let us try and think where she might have gone.'

Their ruminations were cut short by the arrival of General Franklin, intent on bringing both granddaughters to heel.

'Where is Amanda?' he asked imperiously after Roxanne made a belated and distracted appearance in the parlour.

'At the moment she is out, Grandfather,' Roxanne replied.

The general's brows beetled into a thick black line. 'Out?' he roared. 'Didn't I make clear that I would be coming at this time to speak to you both?'

'Yes, I know, but Grandfather... Oh, why do I dissemble? You are bound to discover the truth, and I am so worried. You may even be of help. Amanda's run off.'

'Run off? When?'

'I don't know precisely,' Roxanne admitted. 'It must have happened last night.'

'You don't know?' the general demanded. 'Haven't you taken precautions against such an occurrence? You know she is prone to running away. That's the reason we removed her from Miss Thompson's School!'

'I saw no reason to take precautions, as you put it,' Roxanne said, looking harassed. 'We got along comfortably enough in our weeks together. And I think Amanda ran off only because of those threats you uttered last night. If anyone is to blame, it's you!'

The general, a noted strategist, appeared taken aback by this frontal attack. 'Now see here,' he said.

Roxanne, however, was not about to be silenced. 'Anyone but a corkbrain could have seen how a sensitive child like Amanda would react to your threats.'

'That is enough,' the general snapped, rising to his feet and towering above her. 'I am your grandfather, I should like to remind you. And you will bide your tongue.'

She lifted her chin. 'Or what? Do you propose to do something barbaric such as cutting it off?'

'No, but I can throw you out of here,' he told her. 'I own the lease of this house.'

'That threat has no bark left to it,' she said. 'I choose to leave of my own volition. I am over twenty-one, Grandfather, and am not your charge. I never was.'

'You'll starve to death, pea-goose!'

'I shall manage.'

He snorted. 'Do what you want. What a waste of time this has been. I wash my hands of the pair of you. Skittlebrained females! This never would have happened if you had been boys.' On that note, he left.

As soon as he disappeared out of the door, Roxanne sank back in her Windsor chair. Never had she intended so stormy an exchange. It was most out of character for her. But Grandfather had been so vexatious! And insulting! Treating her like a child! And then there was his shabby treatment of Stanwyck the night before, which she could not condone.

She rose abruptly. There was too much to do to waste her time indulging in an angry fit over her grandfather. Amanda must be found, and she must find a new roof over her own head. As she attempted to decide which of these two thorny problems she ought to tackle first, the Marquis was announced.

'I don't need to ask if the general has been here,' Stanwyck said, taking her hand. 'I passed him in the drive. I can see from your face that he has lost none of his ill temper.'

'Lord Stanwyck,' Roxanne said, feeling a sense of relief that he was at hand, 'I am so glad to see you. I need your advice.'

'I am at your disposal.'

'Tell me how should I go about contacting the Runners.'

His eyes narrowed. 'Do you mean Bow Street, ma'am?'

She nodded.

'Has a crime been committed?' he asked at once.

'I'm not certain,' she told him, frowning. 'If you asked Grandfather, he'd say yes. But then Amanda would say no, and technically she should know better than anyone.'

'Miss Franklin, what the devil are you speaking of?' he demanded.

She appeared surprised at the anxiety in his voice. 'Oh, pray, do you think I have gone mad?' She choked on a laugh. 'It's Amanda. She's run off.'

'Run off?'

'Last night, and pray don't *you* say it's my fault for not knowing the precise hour! She took Kate, so I'm hoping she can't have been too befuddled. Only where could she be?' A sudden hope rose in her breast. 'She didn't apply to you by chance, did she? I swear I shouldn't betray her whereabouts if she did.'

'I wish she had,' Stanwyck said gently.

Her heart sank. 'Do you think she might have gone to Lady Laura?'

'She might have,' he admitted. 'I shall go and check while you stay here.'

'Yes, but that's another thing. I can't stay here. Grandfather and I had a horrid spat. I told him I didn't wish to remain under his protection.'

'I don't blame you,' he said with ready sympathy. 'But where do you propose to go?'

'I don't know. It all came to a head so quickly. My quarrel with Grandfather, I mean. Perhaps Lady Bisbane will take me in. I know she's not due to deliver yet.'

Stanwyck, however, was shaking his head. 'Bisbane is as jumpy as one of his hunters,' he informed her. 'You'd best wait until the babe arrives.'

She thought harder. 'Then perhaps Lady Laura might put me up temporarily?'

'You left early last evening,' he told her. 'Laura, by the end of her triumphant night, was in such a good mood she agreed to house a full contingent of Mrs Lovelace's orphans. They are passing through London on their way to a new home in Scotland. No, we can't have you staying there. Nor,' he said, stroking his chin, 'can I put you up with me at Berkeley Square. I am a male, and we are not related. A pity Gwen is still out of town.' He snapped his fingers. 'I have it. You'll stay in one of the houses I hold a lease on. It's rather Spartan, and doesn't have more than a few sticks of furniture.'

'I don't care,' she said, too relieved at the prospect of a roof over her head to quibble about furniture.

'It's in Upper Wimpole Street,' he warned. 'Not the fashionable area of town.'

'Nor is this,' she said with a smile, waving her hands about the parlour.

'I shall return home immediately and get the key from Stevens. While I do that, you pack your things. I trust you'll bring a maid?'

She laughed. 'Despite Grandfather's words, I am not yet sunk beneath reproach. I hope I can persuade Jennie to come with me.'

He left her to this task as well as the thousand and one other details that needed her attention in the wake of so imminent a departure. Jennie was willing to make the move with her to Upper Wimpole Street, and the next hour passed with the two frantically packing their belongings as well as Amanda's and Kate's.

The Marquis secured the key to the house in Upper Wimpole Street from his secretary, who was too well bred to enquire who his newest *chère amie* might be and why he had seen fit to house her in Upper Wimpole Street, of all places. Then Stanwyck popped in on Laura. His arrival coincided with that of the orphans, all forty-eight of them, and he was obliged to shout over their din to make himself heard. He soon discovered that Laura had not seen Amanda since the performance.

He carried this news back to Roxanne, along with the keys. He was accompanied by Ben who, learning of the situation, insisted on lending a hand.

'I can help you to move,' he said now to Roxanne.

'Ben, that is kind of you. Lord Stanwyck, are you sure there is no word of Amanda?'

'Not yet,' he said, taking her hand. 'I shall pick up her trail, I promise. She can't have gone far.'

'May I come with you?'

He saw the worry in her green eyes. 'I can probably accomplish more alone,' he said gently.

'You're right, I dare say.' She gave a brave smile that struck the Marquis as forlorn. He gave her hand a squeeze.

'I shall let you know the minute I hear anything,' he promised, and then kissed her hand before leaving once again.

CHAPTER NINE

Now why in thunderation did I do that? Stanwyck wondered as he drove away from Curzon Street. Kissing the hands of ladies was a custom that had passed out of fashion, except with dandies and dowagers. And he certainly had not meant it in a flirtatious way. Miss Franklin, he would wager a monkey, was not the flirtatious sort.

He shook his head, telling himself that he was getting to be a regular barley-straw! No doubt he was making too much of things. Miss Franklin, in her anxiety about Amanda, probably had not paid him a jot of attention.

In this instance, however, Stanwyck was wrong. A veritable shock had passed through Roxanne when the Marquis had bestowed his impulsive salute. And for a minute after his departure she continued to wonder whether he was bent on flirting with her. Then her usual good sense prevailed, and she told herself sternly to stop imagining flirtations where there was only the wish to comfort. Briskly she turned her energies to her removal from Curzon Street to Upper Wimpole Street, ably assisted in this task by Ben, who was more than willing to drive her there.

While she was glad to have his help, she was concerned lest he strain his already injured shoulder.

'Pooh, this is a mere trifle,' the Major said, setting down the portmanteau in the parlour of the house. All the same, Roxanne insisted that she and Jennie share the burden in transporting the other portmanteaux from the carriage into the parlour which, as Stanwyck had warned, was small and sparsely furnished, with only a pair of Windsor chairs and a satinwood sofa. A faint, musty smell hung in the air, and she and Jennie set immediately to opening windows.

'Lucky for you that Stanwyck holds this lease,' Ben said, bustling in with some smaller boxes. 'In the midst of the Season it ain't easy to find accommodation.'

'Is it so peculiar for him to have had the lease?' Roxanne asked.

'Oh, I suppose not,' Ben said, wiping his brow with a handkerchief. 'Some chaps hold two or three.'

'Do they? Why so many?' Roxanne asked, baffled.

'Oh, just in case a female should happen to catch their eye,' Ben said. He clapped a hand to his brow, flushing red. 'Oh, I say, I didn't mean to imply that's what happened between you and Stanwyck!'

She burst out laughing. 'Ben, what an absurd idea! You are speaking of a residence for a demirep. But I can't imagine any high flyer worthy of the name putting up here, can you?'

Ben looked about them, and grinned. 'Lud, no,' he agreed.

'So at the very least my reputation is safe. No one would mistake me for a Cyprian.'

'Oh, no,' he concurred. 'Not that you aren't pretty enough to be one if you wanted to, which you do not . . .' He broke off in some confusion.

She took pity on him and rescued him from his dilemma. 'I know what you mean. No, you must not pick up that box. It is far too heavy. Is it true what Lord Stanwyck said, that you and Laura have a dozen orphans staying with you?'

'If it only were a dozen,' Ben said, grimacing. 'Four dozen is closer to the matter. And I vow their noise is akin to Bedlam! What a pity I can't stay here with you. It would be nice and quiet.' He flushed again. 'Oh, by Jove, what am I saying? I'd better leave before I say something even more stupid.'

She protested that he was no such thing, but did not try too hard to dissuade him from leaving. Although grateful for his assistance, she was fagged from her lack of sleep the night before and her anxiety over Amanda. If she only knew her cousin were safe! Not that she could track her down herself. She had not the slightest notion on how to proceed. It were better to let Stanwyck handle the matter. She sat down in one of the two Windsor chairs, wondering at the way he had taken her troubles upon his shoulders. Unbidden, the memory of his lips pressed lightly against her hand came to mind.

Jennie, coming into the parlour just then and seeing her mistress with a queer expression on her face, took it upon herself to persuade her to lie down in the bed-chamber. Roxanne protested, but she finally agreed to lie down for ten minutes. She quickly dozed off and was awakened by Jennie at two o'clock with the news that the Marquis had reappeared, desiring to see her.

'Have you eaten?' was the first question he put to her when she entered the parlour, still a little groggy from her nap.

'What? Oh, no, I'm not hungry.'

'Just as I feared. But I shan't have you suffering a collapse for want of food. I brought along a picnic hamper.' He gave a rueful smile. 'This ain't exactly a hillock, but it shall have to do.'

'I'm not hungry, my lord.'

'Well, I am,' he said, opening the hamper. 'I worked up a considerable appetite hunting down your young cousin.'

Roxanne clapped her hands. 'You found her!'

He handed her a wedge of cheese and nodded, smiling at her relief.

'Where is she, Stanwyck?' she asked.

'In safe hands, as you'll discover this evening,' he said, sampling some of the cheese himself.

'This evening?' Her voice was thoughtful. 'Why must I wait till then?'

His hands were back in the picnic hamper. 'I thought Henri said he had packed some lemonade in here, but I'm dashed if I can find it. Ah, here it is, at last.' He drew out a flask.

'Stanwyck, will you attend to me?'

'I thought I had. Will you have a chicken leg?' he asked, handing one over.

She gave it a tentative nibble, more to appease him than anything else, and found to her surprise that she was very hungry. She took the lemonade he poured for her, all the while pelting him with questions about Amanda.

'She is all right?' she asked. 'The truth, if you please. I assure you I am strong enough to bear it.'

'The truth?' He laughed. 'Your Amanda is in high gig, and shamelessly unrepentant of any concern her running away may have caused. You may comb her hair for that tonight at Lady Montcalm's ball.'

Roxanne nearly spilled her lemonade down the front of her dress. 'Lady Montcalm's ball? Stanwyck, what are you saying? I can't go to any ball.'

'It's a masquerade, actually,' he said scrupulously. 'You have only to don a mask. Laura will lend you some sort of costume. Amanda will contact you there also in disguise.'

'Why can't she contact me here?' Roxanne asked, unable to see the purpose behind the masquerade.

He grimaced. 'I talked until I was blue in the face, Miss Franklin. It seems Amanda has a bee in her bonnet about your grandfather. She's convinced he'll spy on you here. This was the only method I could contrive to answer. I knew you would wish to determine for yourself her well-being and not merely rely on my saying so.' He paused, a half-eaten chicken leg between his fingers. 'I suppose others might have thought of a better method, but Gwen always has said I had not an ounce of imagination.'

Conscious of all his efforts on her behalf, Roxanne felt a pang of guilt. What an ungrateful wretch she was!

'It's just that I never dreamed I would attend a ball in London, especially a masquerade.'

'A masquerade is the best type of ball to attend,' he told her kindly. 'Everyone is busy trying to conceal his identity and discover everyone else's. They won't bother with their usual pretensions. Now, finish up that chicken leg and take the rest of the lemonade.'

She followed his instructions.

'Will you be at the masquerade?' Roxanne asked as he prepared to take his leave.

He looked down at her, hamper in hand. 'Did you think I was going to desert you in your hour of need? Silly goose.' His forefinger flicked lightly under her chin. 'I shall take you there myself. I shall wear a black domino. You can identify me thus if we ever get separated at the ball.'

The Marquis, as Roxanne discovered that evening, cut quite a magnificent swatch in his black domino. With his height, jet-black hair and rugged torso he looked quite the most impressive man she had ever accompanied, not that she was in the habit of accompanying even unimpressive gentlemen anywhere!

Her own costume was a gipsy dress, complete with a red scarf, gold bracelet, and hooped earrings so heavy that they threatened to pull her lobes off.

'I wish the evening were over,' she told him as they settled into his carriage.

'Am I so wanting as a companion after only ten minutes, Miss Franklin?' he quizzed.

A guilty look sprang to her eyes before she recognised the twinkle in his. 'I didn't mean to suggest that, and you know it. It's just that when I think of walking in, cool as you please, to the ball, I begin to quake. I don't even know Lady Montcalm. What if she should discover me?'

'She won't. That's the beauty of a masquerade. She won't know who you are until midnight. By then, we'll have gone. Besides, I'll be close at hand.'

'Yes, I know,' she said, comforted once again by his presence.

The vehicle soon came to a stop in front of the Montcalms' handsome Palladian residence. Hastily Roxanne secured her mask. Stanwyck's was already in place, and the two mounted the tall stately stairs that led to the glittering ballroom.

'Courage,' he murmured as they paused on the threshold to look at the swirling couples. Beautiful princesses waltzed by in the arms of gnomes. One guest had come in the guise of Father Christmas with two large pillows over his stomach. Roxanne inhaled a breath and followed Stanwyck's black domino.

'Ah, lovely gipsy, come and tell my fortune,' a voice entreated as a huntsman approached. Roxanne's first impulse was to recoil, but when she saw how his costume

fitted imperfectly over his arm and the blue eyes twinkling behind the mask, she knew it could only be Ben.

'How did you guess?' he complained, when she put
the question to him. 'I thought I would mystify everyone.
I even shaved off my beard.' As he had been speaking,
he led her out towards the centre of the room.

'What are you doing?' she asked, stopping abruptly.

'Dancing with you,' he replied. 'Don't worry about
Nigel. He'll be there when we're finished. Fortunately
Laura told me what you'd be wearing or I shouldn't have
known you from Eve. You dance well.'

'For a provincial, do you mean?' she quizzed.

He flushed. 'No, I didn't mean to imply that.'

'I know.' She chuckled. 'I was merely roasting you.
And I did have a first-rate dancing-master.'

That was, however, before her father had fallen ill,
when she still had hopes of a Season in London. Odd
that it had taken her more than seven years to find herself
dancing at a London ball. When the waltz ended, she
and Ben were on the far side of the ballroom from
Stanwyck. Before they could make their way back to the
Marquis, a silver-haired Roman importuned Roxanne
for the quadrille.

'Go ahead,' Ben coaxed as she hesitated. 'It's a ball,
remember?'

Swept up in the intoxicating music and excitement all
around, Roxanne acquiesced and danced off with her
new partner.

'Where is Miss Franklin?' a voice hissed in Ben's ear
a moment later. The Major turned to find a black
domino at her side.

'Is that you, Stanwyck?'

'Of course it's me,' the Marquis snapped. 'And answer my question, Bentley. First you waltz off with her from under my nose, and now I find you without her.'

'Oh, she's off dancing with that Roman.' Ben waved a languid hand towards the milling crowd.

'You fool, couldn't you have prevented it?'

'Why should I have?' Ben asked, rather astonished. 'It's a ball, after all. There's no call to be in a pucker, Stanwyck. Roxanne told me some time ago that she wouldn't be going to any balls or parties. She's entitled to some enjoyment.'

'Fustian!' the Marquis snapped. 'She is a green girl, and as such, my responsibility. I'll thank you to remember that before you usurp my position again.'

'I didn't know you had a position with Roxanne,' the Major said naively.

Stanwyck looked nettled even with his mask on. 'I consider myself responsible for her.'

'Very well. But she won't come to harm in the ballroom. By the by, when is Amanda arriving?'

'Soon, I hope. And in the guise of a poor little match-girl. Keep your eyes open for her, will you?'

The quadrille ended, but before either Ben or Stanwyck could make his way to Roxanne, she was being coaxed by a tall sheikh into having a turn on the floor with him. After the Arab came a learned barrister complete with wig.

'Enjoying yourself?' a voice asked her during one lull. She jumped before she recognised the black domino.

'Oh, Stanwyck.' She pressed a hand to her throat. 'You frightened me.'

'I beg your pardon.' His voice softened at once. 'I didn't mean to bite your head off, but I thought you should know that Amanda has arrived. Do you still wish for a word with her?'

She was stricken by conscience. She had been so caught up with the festivities that she had very nearly forgotten what had prompted her visit to the Montcalms' ball.

'Where is she?' she asked anxiously.

'Wait in that anteroom,' he said, nodding towards a corner. 'I'll send her to you.'

A few minutes later Roxanne sat impatiently on an Egyptian settee counting the cherubs on the painted ceiling. She had reached thirty-two when the door opened and a little match-girl popped her head in.

'Cousin Roxanne?' she whispered.

'Amanda, is that you?' Roxanne asked doubtfully.

Amanda ran into her arms. 'Yes. I wasn't sure at first it was you. I vow you look like a gipsy. And isn't my costume frightful!' She giggled. 'I vow, if Grandfather saw me he wouldn't have the slightest way of recognising me!'

'I should hope not,' Roxanne said, shuddering at the very notion of the general's reaction to his grand-daughter as a match-girl, coming on the heels of her appearance as Bottom.

'Why did you run away, Amanda?' she asked, giving her cousin a little shake. 'And where have you gone?'

'I couldn't bear to live in a convent, Roxanne,' Amanda explained, two spots of colour burning bright in her cheeks. 'I knew Grandfather would clap me in one just as he threatened.'

'That was mere flourishing. But where are you staying?'

'With Agatha Melville.'

Roxanne frowned. 'The Melvilles?'

'Agatha was in the theatricals with me,' Amanda explained.

Roxanne's brows cleared. 'One of your chums from the troupe?'

'Yes, exactly! And she comes from a most excellent family, or else Lady Laura would never have allowed her to take part in the theatricals. She is a month older than me, and of course when I explained how it would be in a convent, she understood. She invited me and Kate to stay with her.'

'And what Banbury tale did she tell her parents?' Roxanne quizzed.

Amanda looked momentarily abashed. 'We didn't need to, actually. They are away in Buckinghamshire. A governess is looking after Agatha.' Amanda giggled. 'The poor dear is so short-sighted. And it will be temporary.'

'Amanda, you mustn't intrude on the Melvilles any longer. Come and stay with me.'

Amanda shook her head emphatically, and her face took on that mulish expression Roxanne knew so well. 'I shall never set foot in Curzon Street again.'

'Hasn't Stanwyck told you? I am at Upper Wimpole Street instead. Grandfather and I practically came to cuffs.'

'Cousin Roxanne,' Amanda crowed in obvious delight, 'you ran off, too?'

Roxanne chuckled. 'I suppose I have. So you see, you can stay safely with me.'

Amanda considered this. When she spoke again, her tone was thoughtful but no less adamant. 'Grandfather may yet discover your whereabouts. And if I'm with you, he'll have no compunction about throwing me into that convent.'

'No, he won't. He washed his hands of the pair of us. He said so himself. And, really, he isn't your guardian. Aunt Peg is.'

Amanda snorted. 'Aunt Peg is dotty and will do whatever Grandfather wants.'

'Perhaps not,' Roxanne said. She herself had always enjoyed good relations with their aunt and hoped to be able to persuade her to leave Amanda in her care.

'I'd liefer stay with the Melvilles.'

'But what will happen when Agatha's parents return, as they must sooner or later?'

Amanda shrugged. 'I shall find somewhere else.'

'You could go to Aunt Peg.' At Amanda's horrified stare, she quickly added, 'She's not so bad.'

'But she lives in York,' Amanda wailed.

'That's not so far away these days.'

'It is to me. I shan't be able to see Freddie.'

'Who is Freddie?' Roxanne asked.

For the first time that evening Amanda hesitated, and through the dirt that constituted her match-girl's make-up, Roxanne discerned a veritable blush. Amanda blushing at anything was certainly a novel occurrence.

'He's my friend,' Amanda said finally. 'Oh, bother that! He's more than a friend. Promise me you won't laugh, Roxanne,' she pleaded.

'Of course I shan't laugh, my dear,' Roxanne said, gazing into the intent little face.

'I quite love him,' Amanda announced. 'He's so different from anyone I've ever met before. He's a play-wright, and is so proud and penniless, that goes without saying. And he's written the most marvellous play. I'd tell you the name, but he keeps changing it. And if we could only find a patron for it I know it would be a huge triumph. Frederic Devens will be as great a name some day as Mr Sheridan's.'

'Amanda, are you roasting me?'

Amanda looked shocked. 'It's the truth! Freddie is also quite handsome. You'd like him, I know, Roxanne. I nearly persuaded him to come with me tonight and meet you. But he is so shy.'

'Am I to assume that Mr Devens has made you a declaration?' Roxanne asked, digesting the reality of Amanda in love.

Amanda gave her head a sad little shake. 'No, he's too proud, since his pockets are to let. And yet I know he loves me from the look in his eyes. It's just that he thinks I'm too young for a serious declaration,' she said matter-of-factly. 'Which is too stupid, for I'm nearly seventeen!'

Roxanne laughed. 'Practically an old woman,' she agreed.

Amanda looked sheepish. 'And, so you see, I can't go off to York now, when things are developing so nicely.'

Roxanne thought through her next words with particular care. 'Amanda, you haven't been indiscreet, I should hope? With young Freddie, I mean?'

'Oh no, Roxanne.' Amanda gave a rueful laugh. 'Half the time all Freddie does is talk about his play and his plans for it. His family have cut him off since he's decided to be an artist. The other half of the time I spend telling him about the famous actress I hope to be. It's quite congenial.'

Roxanne was not so certain about the congeniality but then turned to another, more pressing, point. 'Do you need any funds?'

'The Marquis gave me some money when he found me this morning. I must say it was clever of him to find me through Agatha, and I think this masquerade was a clever notion, too. He's not so fusty, despite his age. And now I must go, for Kate is waiting outside for me.'

Roxanne kissed her. 'Promise me to send word at once if you are in any danger or want for anything.'

'I promise, but I shan't be in any danger,' Amanda said blithely, and left.

For a moment Roxanne sat alone in the anteroom, absorbing all that had been said. Could Amanda really be in love? It had to be a mistake, a mere schoolgirl crush, serious at the time and then easily forgotten. The door opened, and as she caught a glimpse of a black domino, she hastily composed herself.

'How did the interview go?' he asked.

'Fine, all in all,' she said, deciding not to tell him about Amanda's new love. 'Except who, pray, are the Melvilles?'

'Quite a respectable family. I wouldn't have let Amanda stay, were they not. I paid a call on some of the regulars in Laura's theatrical group, asking if Amanda had made any one particular friend during that week. I soon came up with young Miss Melville. Further enquiry led me to the information that her parents were out of town. It wasn't hard to piece together what had undoubtedly occurred. I found the governess a ninny-hammer who quite dotes on her young charge. I dare say Amanda had no difficulty in pulling the wool over her eyes.'

'Amanda tells me you lent her some money. I must repay you.'

He looked mildly amused. 'My good Miss Franklin, that would be quite insulting.'

'Oh, I didn't know that,' she said, stricken. 'I didn't mean to offend you.'

'Good. That's settled, I hope. By the by, I left a footman at the Melville residence to keep an eye on her.'

Roxanne sighed. 'That was good of you.' She gave a little laugh. 'I keep saying that, and I keep thanking you, it seems. And now that that is over, we can leave, I suppose?'

'If you wish. But you needn't be in such a hurry. It's not even close to midnight. And no one suspects a thing. You haven't even had any champagne. Allow me to procure a glass for you.'

He was gone on the instant, and she sat, happily enough, wondering at all his kindnesses. How could she ever repay him when the very mention of it had been taken as an affront? But somehow she must contrive a way. As she mulled over the problem, the door opened, and she saw him return without the glass of champagne.

'Were they out of champagne, Stanwyck?' she asked.

He nodded.

'It's just as well. We'd better go. I own to being somewhat fatigued. A consequence of the long day, I suppose.'

He bowed and offered her his hand, which she took. Then to her utter astonishment he grabbed her and pulled her boldly into his arms, kissing her full on the lips.

This was no gentle kiss but a cruel raking of his mouth on hers. His hands dug into her arms, and she struggled against him, to no avail. Finally, when he released her, she stepped back and slapped him hard on the cheek. He absorbed the blow without flinching, threw back his dark head, and laughed. With that mocking sound ringing in her ears, she ran out of the anteroom.

CHAPTER TEN

'I SAY, Roxanne, do you know that you dropped an earring?' Benjamin asked, picking a gold hoop from the floor.

'Ben, thank heavens!' Roxanne clung to the Major's arm. 'I beg you to take me home at once.'

'But I thought Stanwyck brought you,' Ben said, wary of cutting out the Marquis now that he knew Nigel considered Roxanne his responsibility.

'I don't want to have a thing to do with the Marquis ever again,' Roxanne replied, blinking back tears to Ben's astonishment. He never would have called her the vapourish sort.

'Good heavens. Er, don't you want your earring?' he asked, holding it out. 'And what the deuce has Stanwyck done to you?'

'It was *horrid*, Ben! He tried . . .' Roxanne's voice disappeared into a quaver. She tried again. 'He attempted to make love to me in that anteroom.'

'*What?*' Ben expostulated.

'I know it's not the sort of topic a man and woman discuss, so you must promise you won't ever repeat it. I never wish to see him again!'

'Yes, but look here, it must be a mistake. Stanwyck's been in the refreshment-room all this time. See for yourself. There he comes!' He pointed with relief to the familiar black domino making his way carefully across the ballroom carrying two glasses of champagne.

The Marquis needed only a second to deduce that something was very wrong. 'What's amiss?' he demanded, taking in Roxanne's heightened colour and the quizzing look from Ben.

'You're bringing me champagne,' Roxanne said blankly.

He stared at her. 'Yes. Have you changed your mind then about taking a glass?'

She shook her head, then looked at Ben. 'I don't understand.'

'That makes a pair of us,' Stanwyck said. 'What has happened to put you on end?'

'A man in the anteroom,' Roxanne whispered, scarcely daring to look the Marquis full in the face. 'He wore a black domino exactly like yours. His height, his hair—everything was identical. But it couldn't be you, if you were procuring the glasses of champagne.'

The Marquis was not greatly enlightened by this statement, which he thought bordered on the idiotish. And yet he was not prone to think her dull-witted.

'Miss Franklin had an ugly encounter with someone in the anteroom whom she mistook for you,' Ben said quickly.

'Did she, by Jove?' the Marquis said. His mouth was set in grim lines. 'We shall see who is pretending to be me!' With that, he thrust the champagne glasses at Ben and marched across the floor toward the anteroom. Roxanne followed. Stanwyck flung the door open, surprising one of Lady Montcalm's daughters, who was engaged in a vigorous flirtation with a suitor. Giggling, the young couple ran out of the room.

'Whoever it was has evidently gone,' Stanwyck said, making a quick search of the empty chamber.

'He wore a black domino,' Roxanne repeated.

'How many black dominoes are present this evening, Ben?' Stanwyck asked the major, who had followed them in.

'Four or five, counting you, I suppose,' Ben replied, putting the champagne glasses down on a pier table.

'I must find the one who has insulted Miss Franklin,' Nigel said.

He looked so fierce that Roxanne felt a pang of real alarm. She knew his reputation as a crack shot.

'It's all right, Stanwyck,' she hastened to assure him. 'I'm not distressed any more now that I know it wasn't you—who did what he did,' she finished lamely, hoping that he would not ask her to elaborate.

'Would you like the champagne now?' he asked quietly.

She shook her head. 'Would you mind terribly if I asked to return to Upper Wimpole Street?'

'No, certainly not,' Stanwyck said.

She was quiet in the carriage, and the Marquis did not intrude on her privacy by asking unnecessary questions. He had his own thoughts to concern him during the ride. Mistaken identities were commonplace at masquerades and contributed to the frivolous air that usually surrounded such a ball. But he could not help feeling that the incident in the anteroom was not as innocent as it might appear.

He said nothing of this to Roxanne, but after seeing her safely in at Upper Wimpole Street, he chose to return to the masquerade. The first one he saw when he strode back into Lady Montcalm's ballroom was Ben.

'Have you found out anything useful?' he demanded.

'Stanwyck, is that you?' Ben asked suspiciously.

The Marquis sighed. 'Perhaps we ought to adopt a password, the way they did during the war. What progress have you made on the other black dominoes?'

'Two are short and fat. They can be scotched. The other one is standing in that corner.' He nodded in the direction of a tall, dark-haired gentleman. Stanwyck followed his gaze.

'I'll go over and have a word with him.'

'Wait, Stanwyck, let me,' Ben said. 'Whoever played that hoax on Miss Franklin knew she mistook him for you. He might become suspicious if another black domino interrogated him.'

The Major's suggestion made sense. 'Go then, quickly,' Stanwyck urged.

As Ben made his way towards the other black domino, Stanwyck waited, arms crossed on his chest. He was still standing there when he felt a good-natured poke from a fan. He turned.

'Hello, Black Domino,' said a husky-voiced lady clad in shimmering gold.

'Hello, Princess,' he returned.

'Actually, it's Cinderella.'

'Now that shan't do,' he said, an ironic gleam in his eye. 'No one would believe that Sally Jersey ever lived in cinders. And as for her being a slave to her sisters...'

The Patroness gave a tinkle of laughter that turned into a sigh of despair. 'You are the fifth person to have discovered my identity. Why do I bother to attend these stupid masquerades?'

Stanwyck laughed. 'Perhaps you ought to wear a different costume next time, Sally. You always come as Cinderella.'

'That's true enough,' she conceded. 'Such a want of originality! And now it is my turn to do the guessing,

Black Domino. Tall, muscular—handsome, too, I have no doubt. You wouldn't be Webbe now, would you?'

'Your eyesight plays tricks, dear Sally,' the Marquis retorted. 'Webbe is a blond.'

'The joke is on you, Black Domino. I distinctly over-heard Webbe the other day telling another that he planned to dye his hair for this occasion.'

'Did he now?' Stanwyck spoke quietly and moved off before the Patroness could delve further into his identity.

Lady Jersey might be a shatterbrain, but she had given him considerable food for thought. Was Webbe the black domino who had importuned Miss Franklin in the anteroom? Ben returned as he mulled over this question.

'Well?' Stanwyck demanded.

'I wouldn't wager my life on it, mind, but I have the uncanny notion that the black domino is Webbe. But the hair doesn't match.'

'Forget the hair for the moment. What makes you think it's Webbe?'

Benjamin made a face. 'I saw him take a pinch of snuff. You know how he mixes his own, and it reeks to high heaven. An unmistakable scent.'

'Yes, I know,' the Marquis said, remembering the brief pinch he had sampled.

'And,' Ben continued, 'I saw him blush and move away when Lord Prescott asked if anyone had seen Webbe's expensive Arabian yet in the Park.'

'Promising, but hardly proof.'

Ben shrugged. 'This ain't a courtroom, after all. And if you want confirmation, all we need do is stay on until midnight. What do you plan to do if it was Webbe who insulted Miss Franklin? If it's Paddington Green, you'll let me stand you second, I hope? My shoulder is com-pletely healed.'

This thirst for bloodshed was openly deplored by the Marquis.

Ben looked amazed. 'Do you mean you aren't going to avenge the slight done to Miss Franklin?'

'Paddington was my first inclination,' Stanwyck agreed, 'but I've been thinking of Miss Franklin. Calling Webbe out might prove a greater embarrassment to her.'

'You're going to let him get off scot free?'

The Marquis gave a grim smile. 'Not for long, that I promise! There shall come a time when I shall call Webbe to account for all the harm he has done to me and those about me.'

Ben was not completely persuaded, but he could do nothing to change the Marquis's mind, and Stanwyck went off to take his leave. He was prevented from doing this immediately by the approach of Lady Montcalm, who as the hostess had decided to eschew a mask for herself.

'Ah, Black Domino,' she greeted, her feathered turban dipping in his direction. 'You can't be going so soon. Don't tell me my ball is a dreary bore.'

'On the contrary, Letitia, it is first rate, as always. I congratulate you.'

Lady Montcalm looked gratified as she fanned herself with an ivory-handled fan. 'It *is* Stanwyck, isn't it?'

He saw no reason to hide his identity any longer. He was planning to leave the ball. 'Yes, it's Stanwyck.'

'Have you seen her yet, Stanwyck?'

'Her?' He was baffled.

Lady Montcalm drew him aside and snapped her fan shut. 'I vow I was hoping you would turn up tonight. I can't keep the secret until midnight.'

The frown on Stanwyck's face cleared. 'What is this?' he said quizzingly. 'Have you taken yet another new Beauty under your wing?'

'Not exactly a new one, my lord,' she said, chuckling, and gave him a nudge in the direction of a tall lady dressed in green. 'Doesn't Scheherazade look familiar, Nigel?'

Obediently he looked at the woman in green. For a moment he felt his heart skip a beat. She wore an emerald necklace which looked vaguely familiar. But it was not possible. He clenched his fists. It could not be!

'It's Dru, Stanwyck,' Lady Montcalm said softly in his ear.

'Drusilla? By heaven, it can't be.'

'Is that all you can say?' she demanded.

He turned, the spell now broken, and looked into his hostess's eyes. 'What ought I to say?'

She shrugged. 'My word, I don't know. I'm not the one who has worn the willow for her all these years. But I had expected something a shade more dramatic from you. Not a swoon, but aren't you even going to ask her to dance?'

'Ask Drusilla to dance?'

Lady Montcalm sighed and tucked an ostrich-feather back into her turban. 'It's hardly an unusual request in a ballroom, Stanwyck!'

'What is she doing here?' he demanded brusquely.

'She has just returned from America.'

'And where is Robert?'

Lady Montcalm sobered. 'Alas, he's dead. It happened two years ago in Philadelphia. None of us here in the family knew of it. But then mail is slow, and Drusilla was never the best of correspondents. She decided her life would be better here. She never really took to the colonies, which I quite understand. She returned this week. But she's not a mourning widow, by any means.' As Stanwyck continued to look blankly at her, she grew even more exasperated.

'Are you going to stand like a stock?' she demanded. 'Aren't you going over to talk to her? Do you think it was a simple task to unearth that dress she insisted on wearing tonight on the mere chance that you might come?' She gave him a little push. 'It's only Drusilla, Nigel. She hasn't changed that much. She shan't eat you.'

Just how it happened Stanwyck could not have said, even if his life depended on it. But he soon found himself standing next to Scheherazade. Could it really be Drusilla after all these years?

'Good evening, Black Domino,' she said, and all his doubts vanished. The lilting voice, the sturdy little chin that the mask could not hide. It was unmistakably Dru.

'Good evening, Lady in Green,' he retorted.

The smile on her face faded a little, and he saw the marked hesitation in the green eyes behind the mask.

'Nigel?' she whispered.

'How have you been, Drusilla?'

She tossed her head back in the carefree manner he remembered so vividly.

'Do you know, Nigel, that when I imagined our meeting again I thought of all manner of witty things that I would undoubtedly say. And now that I have you here, I find they have withered on my tongue.'

'Perhaps we shouldn't speak, but merely dance,' he suggested and held a hand out to her.

'You are still the cool one, aren't you, Stanwyck,' she said with a laugh as they began to waltz.

He glanced down at the upturned nose. 'Am I?'

'You have an answer for everything,' she accused.

'Hardly that. For instance, I don't even know when you returned to London.'

'Two days ago,' she supplied at once. 'I'm staying here with Cousin Letitia.' Her voice fell. 'Did she mention Robert?'

'Yes, I'm sorry.'

She sighed and shrugged a dainty shoulder. 'It happened two years ago. And, in truth, Robert wasn't the man I thought he was when I married him. That goes without saying, since I chose him over you. I was greatly deceived. Infamous to say such a thing now that he is dead.'

'Why did you leave Philadelphia?' he asked as they circled the room. The others dancing might have been wraiths for all the attention he paid them. All he knew at the moment was Drusilla.

'There was nothing for me there,' she explained. 'And I missed England, far more than you could imagine.'

'And England missed you.'

She smiled at his gallantry. 'Just England, Nigel? Dare I hope that you missed me just a trifle?'

A muscle worked in his jaw, and when he spoke it was not without difficulty. 'I missed you, Drusilla. Far more than just a trifle. But you made your decision. I was obliged to respect it.'

'Such an honourable sort you are, Nigel. That always vexed me beyond belief. When I told you I had chosen Robert, all you did was bow and leave.'

'Coaxing and cajoling were never my style,' he reminded her. 'I made my offer. You refused it.'

'Pray don't remind me,' she implored. 'If you only knew how often I've wondered what it would have been like being married to you instead of to Robert.'

He twisted his lips in an ironic smile. 'You wouldn't have gone off to America, of that you may be certain.'

She laughed with him. 'I must admit I was *floored* when he sprung that on me so soon after our honeymoon. I had no idea he was addicted to travelling. The New World! Bah, that's what I say.'

'I trust you took the ton there by storm.'

'There is no ton there, Nigel,' she said witheringly. 'And I don't miss Philadelphia at all.'

'I'm sorry about Robert,' he said truthfully.

A serious look replaced the gaiety in her eyes. 'It was a carriage accident. Two years ago next Christmas. It took me nearly a year to settle things and then to decide what to do with myself. I finally came to the conclusion that my home was here in England.'

'I'm glad,' he said simply.

She sighed and relaxed in his arms. 'Do you know I had Cousin Letitia search high and low for this dress? I left a few of my possessions with her when I emigrated.'

'I recognised it at once,' he said. 'You wore it the last time we danced together.'

'That was the same evening you gave me these emeralds.' Her fingers lightly caressed the jewels about her throat. 'It was so generous of you, especially since I had already told you I had accepted Robert's offer. But then, you were never the purse-squeeze he was.'

The waltz had ended, and he escorted her off, thinking of all the years that had gone by. And Drusilla was now free to marry again. Did he dare to speculate further?

'Is there any champagne, Nigel?' she asked. 'I own to a thirst.'

Obediently he went off to the refreshment-room, glad for the opportunity to collect his thoughts. The last few minutes seemed the stuff of impossible dreams, the sort of dreams he had not indulged in after Dru had sailed for America. And now here she was back in London. She would now be twenty-six, but she looked hardly a day over twenty!

He took the two glasses of champagne back into the ballroom. Drusilla was not in the chair where he had left her. Frowning, his eyes searched the room until he found her dancing with another black domino. Was it Webbe, bent on mischief again? he wondered.

When the quadrille ended, he approached the pair, still carrying the glasses of champagne. 'I believe you wanted a drink, Drusilla,' he said mildly.

'Stanwyck?' The note of incredulity rose in her voice as her eyes shifted from one black domino to the other. 'I could have sworn...I thought I was dancing with you!'

'A mistake that is reasonable, given your lengthy absence. Champagne?'

'Yes, of course!' She took the glass from him. 'But if you're Stanwyck, then who...?' She gazed at the other black domino.

'Allow me to introduce Viscount Webbe, who appears to have a penchant this evening for stealing a march on me whenever I go off for champagne,' the Marquis said knowingly.

'You take the fun out of a masquerade, Stanwyck,' Webbe complained. 'At your service, Lady in Green.'

'Two black dominoes of the same height and colouring,' Drusilla murmured. 'Who would have thought it?'

'Ordinarily no one,' Stanwyck answered. 'Webbe is blond usually. He dyed his hair black.'

'I thought it would be amusing,' Webbe replied easily. 'Do you have some quarrel with it, Stanwyck?'

'Certainly not,' the Marquis replied. 'But what will you do if the dye doesn't come out of your hair?'

'I hope you're wrong about the dye, Nigel,' Drusilla murmured, as Webbe departed in a huff. 'I accepted an invitation to ride in the Park with him later this week, thinking he was you. How very odd he shall look with his hair blackened that way. It's all very well for a masquerade, but it's bound to look peculiar in daylight.'

Stanwyck laughed. 'It will serve him with his own sauce.'

Drusilla fluttered her eyelashes. 'Jealous, Nigel?'

'Good God, no! The day I am jealous of Webbe...' He gave a scornful laugh.

This answer did not suit Drusilla. Although she had just returned from America, she wished to regain her premier position in the ton, and she would have liked nothing better than to have reduced Stanwyck to the status of a squabbling schoolboy. Squabbling over her, that is.

'Who is he, Nigel?' she asked now, taking a sip of her champagne. He had already finished his. 'I don't believe I met him before when I was in London.'

'Probably not. He came into the viscountcy by the back door. An uncle's death and then two of his cousins.'

'Rich?'

'Oh, lud, yes!'

She swirled her champagne on her tongue. 'What does he look like unmasked, I wonder?'

'The females are of the usual opinion that he is handsome,' he replied indifferently. 'But if you stay on till midnight, you can discover this for yourself.'

She handed him the empty champagne glass. 'Is it my imagination, Nigel? I get the distinct impression that you dislike Webbe.'

'We have had our differences of late. He's hardly a bosom bow.'

'How intriguing. I would have thought that two men of fashion such as yourselves would find a good deal of mutual interest.'

'Such is not the case.'

'I hope you're not displeased that I will be riding in the Park with him.'

He smiled. 'You're a grown woman, Dru. I wouldn't dream of dictating to you whom you should or should not see.'

Stanwyck left the ball an hour later. Lady Montcalm immediately made a beeline for her cousin.

'Well, my dear, how did it go? I am on pins and needles to hear all of it.'

Drusilla flashed a most superior smile. 'Much better than I had expected, Cousin Letitia. I believe I have the means of making Stanwyck jealous. Thanks to a certain viscount.'

Lady Montcalm was as shrewd as they come.

'Do you mean Webbe?'

'I do. They seem to have a hearty dislike of each other.'

Her cousin laughed. 'That's an understatement. They are always at dagger points. Webbe beat Stanwyck in the bidding for a prize Arabian at Tattersall's earlier in the week. How the fur flew over that! And there have been other little skirmishes. Petty little things.'

'Well, now that I am here, let's hope the rivalry will cease to be petty and turn serious,' Drusilla drawled, and drained another glass of champagne.

CHAPTER ELEVEN

THE REAPPEARANCE of Drusilla Goodheart caused a ripple of excitement in what had been hitherto a lacklustre Season. Her presence, revealed at midnight at Lady Montcalm's ball, had been received with delight by the other guests, many of whom remembered her as the vivacious Beauty of Seasons past.

Not satisfied with only a perfunctory word or two at the ball, two of Almack's Patronesses descended on Lady Montcalm's residence the following day to determine for themselves the whys and wherefores of Drusilla's return.

The years had not changed her ethereal loveliness. She was, according to Lady Jersey's pronounced view of the matter, the equal of any reigning Beauty, a comment that the Countess Lieven scornfully proclaimed Spanish coin. This Season—as they all knew—had failed to produce the usual bona fide Beauty.

Drusilla was acknowledged to have held up tolerably well, particularly after so lengthy a stay in America. And her high spirits, judging by her surprise appearance at her cousin's masquerade, were just as they used to be. All deemed it unfortunate that Robert had died, but since his family no longer resided in London, and the mishap had occurred two years before, happily Drusilla was not obliged to don widow's weeds.

Within a week of her return, wagers were already being offered as to which gentleman would succeed in winning her, with Stanwyck being accorded the role of the favourite because of his previous acquaintance with her.

'But for all that,' Lady Jersey observed wisely to Maria Sefton, 'Drusilla did ask a good many questions about Webbe!'

The Marquis was not inclined to favour anyone with his own views, if indeed he could say what his own feelings were. Her return *sans* Robert could only be regarded in the light of a minor miracle. The realisation that she was attainable was a heady sensation.

Not that he could woo and win her unchallenged. She was still highly courted. During one morning visit that first week, he discovered that her drawing-room held four other gentlemen besides himself and one besotted poet.

Drusilla was not the only matter of interest to Stanwyck, for the week of her return coincided with yet another propitious arrival, that of Prince from Derbyshire.

'He's a regular Trojan, sir.' Albert could not keep the shine from his eyes as he praised the horse standing before them. 'Not a flaw anywhere. And he bore the trip down very nicely.'

'Good.' The Marquis ran his hands down the horse's flanks. He itched to show him off, but good sense prevailed. It was better to wait until the horse was fully recovered from any ill effects of the trip.

His first venture out on Prince occurred later that week, and it was only a light morning run to the Park. But he enjoyed it immensely. He could not help but notice the amazed looks of the passers-by. No one ventured to speak to him, but before the day was over the prattle-boxes had done their work. The only topic deemed worthy of discussion was Stanwyck's magnificent new mount—with various wagers being placed as to what astronomical price it had commanded.

'A few slow-tops even thought you might have bought Webbe's Arabian from him,' Philip Dudley said to Stanwyck as they walked to White's on Thursday evening. 'He hasn't shown it to anyone.'

'Is that what you think, Philip?'

'Bless me, Nigel, I don't know what to think,' his friend said, amiably as always. 'Be deuced odd of you to buy anything of Webbe's.'

'I'd clap myself in Bedlam first,' the Marquis answered. 'I bought the horse from Lord Julian Smythe of Derbyshire.'

'It must have cost a pretty penny, if what I hear about it is true,' Philip said.

Stanwyck swung his ivory-handled cane. 'Pretty enough,' he said, but Mr Dudley was not to be fobbed off so easily.

'As pretty as Webbe's?' he quizzed.

The Marquis shook his head. 'Not half that much.'

Philip whistled. 'A very good buy then, Nigel.'

'I thought so,' Stanwyck said, looking pleased.

'May I see him before I burst?' his friend demanded.

Stanwyck chuckled at the other man's eagerness. 'I'll ride in the Park again tomorrow if you like.'

'Yes, I do like, but *do* have a heart and don't make it so early in the morning,' Mr Dudley protested. 'Ride in the afternoon at the fashionable hour. I'm not the only one in the city who's interested in seeing your new mount.'

The Marquis graciously yielded to this entreaty. They were nearing the entrance to the club when Philip broached another question. 'By the by, Nigel, is it true you've set up a successor to Mrs Kinney at Upper Wimpole Street, of all places?'

Stanwyck came to a rigid halt by the door to the club. 'Good Jupiter, Philip, the questions you ask! Can you see any self-respecting demirep residing in such a street?'

Philip laughed. ''Pon rep, no. But some swear there's a female living under your protection in the street.'

'A friend of the family who had need of a roof over her head,' Stanwyck explained, 'and a far cry from being Mrs Kinney's successor.'

'Speaking of the fair Fanny, Webbe's given her her *congé*,' Philip informed Stanwyck.

'Has he, now?' They had entered the club. 'That infatuation didn't last long, did it?'

Philip hooted. 'He wasn't infatuated. He just wanted to cut you out with her.'

'Which he did.'

'Only because you were already tired of her. It was only a matter of time.'

'I don't suppose Fanny is crying her heart out over Webbe, is she?' Stanwyck enquired faintly.

Philip roared with laughter. 'She wouldn't be our Fanny then, would she? She met up with young Clampett. You don't know the halfling, so there's no reason to tax your memory. He's wet behind the ears and has a mother who bullocks him. He always struck me as frightened of females. Well, Fanny has taken him under her wing, and the lad is blooming.'

'Fanny always did have a maternal side to her,' Stanwyck observed, grinning. 'Actually, she would have a good deal to teach young Clampett, if he were smart enough to pay attention.'

'Of course he'll pay attention!' Philip was shocked. 'It's his first *affaire*, after all. And she's the first female he's ever seen besides his mother and those bran-faced sisters of his.'

'I'm glad Fanny has something to amuse herself with.'

'Yes, as you must, now that Drusilla is back. I haven't seen her. Is she as beautiful as ever?'

'Drusilla?' The Marquis's voice was thoughtful. 'Beautiful? Without a question, Philip. Without a question.'

On these words they parted, Philip to pursue his interests in the card-room and the Marquis to the reading-room. But his reading of the *Gentleman's Monthly* was interrupted by several beaux who came in to pelt him with questions about his Arabian.

'As long as you didn't beggar yourself like Webbe,' Lord Haverly told him later that evening when he stopped in at the club. 'Half the price Webbe paid, you say?'

'And twice the horse.'

Lord Haverly's moustache twitched. 'I'd give a monkey to see Webbe's face when he sees it.'

'Sees what?' a voice asked urbanely. The two men in the reading-room turned. Webbe stood in the doorway.

'Stanwyck's new horse,' Lord Haverly said after a measuring look at the Viscount. 'An Arabian like yours.'

'Did you find something then, Stanwyck?' Webbe asked, walking over to the fire to warm his hands.

Stanwyck nodded.

'He paid less than half your ten thousand pounds, too,' Haverly could not resist adding.

The Viscount kicked a log in the fireplace. 'Perhaps that's because it's half the horse.'

Lord Haverly drew an involuntary breath and glanced quickly at his brother-in-law. The Marquis's eyes flickered, evidence that he had registered this aspersion to his reputation as a judge of horseflesh.

'You are invited to see for yourself tomorrow at the Park,' Stanwyck said coolly.

'I look forward to it,' Webbe replied just as coolly, and with a mocking bow he left.

'Courteous devil, ain't he?' Lord Haverly snorted. 'I confess to a growing inclination to box his ears.'

Stanwyck laughed, and part of his tension drained. 'Save your strength, Thaddeus. He's not worth it.'

The news that Stanwyck's Arabian could be seen the next afternoon at the Park spread like wildfire throughout the city. Roxanne heard of it from Ben, who drove her there at the appointed hour.

'Wouldn't miss this for the world,' he said, explaining his haste to Roxanne, who had been under the impression that they were bound for a sedate drive. Instead, Ben's carriage rattled and careered over the cobblestones headed for the Park.

'Webbe will be there, too, I'd wager a monkey,' he said, clinging to the reins as his companion clung just as hard to her hat. 'By Jove, I hope Stanwyck's horse is as magnificent as he claims. That would take the wind out of Webbe's sails! No love lost between those two, especially now that Drusilla is back.'

'Drusilla?' Roxanne asked blankly, one hand clapped to the brim of her hat.

Ben turned his face towards her, and she had to smile at the traces of a new beard that was growing. He had regretted almost immediately shaving off his old one. This, despite Laura's acid comment that he resembled a rabblemonger rather than a military officer.

'Yes, haven't you heard? Drusilla's back. Where have you been?'

'At Upper Wimpole Street. Who's this Drusilla?'

'Drusilla Crosby, dash it, I mean Goodheart. She's the one Nigel's been wearing the willow for all these years,' Ben hastened to explain. 'Not that he would ever say he was doing it! She returned to London last week, a widow! Webbe's dangling after her, too. So it's bound to get sticky if it continues.'

'Is she so beautiful?' Roxanne asked wistfully as they entered the Park. She could never imagine any gentlemen fighting over her!

'See for yourself,' Ben exclaimed, spotting Drusilla on a white mare cantering next to the Viscount. 'She's coming this way with Webbe.'

Although Roxanne knew that curiosity was a killer of felines and a deplorable trait in humans, she lost not a second in turning towards the white mare. The woman riding so confidently was flaxen-haired and looked lovely from a distance, and Roxanne had the distressing impression that she would be even lovelier at closer scrutiny.

'Want to see more of her?' Ben asked obligingly. 'I can draw the carriage up easily enough.'

'No, what a notion.' She scotched this plan at once. 'I shouldn't be caught dead gawking at her.'

'Why not?' he asked cheerfully. 'It's what everyone else has been doing since her return.' He brought his vehicle slightly closer.

'Don't you dare introduce us, Ben,' Roxanne whispered.

However, there was no danger of this happening for, as Ben explained, he was a mere nobody to Drusilla, not worth knowing.

'Not in the same league as Stanwyck or Webbe,' he said without a trace of bitterness in his voice. 'Look at Webbe. He is riding his Arabian today. It is magnificent. He rode it to steal Stanwyck's thunder, I'll go bail. And he's got Drusilla with him, too. That's enough to make Stanwyck see daggers.'

The Viscount did look uncommonly pleased with himself as he rode alongside Drusilla. The actual idea of riding together had been hers, but he had fallen in with the suggestion readily. Like everyone else, he knew of her rejection of Stanwyck's offer years ago, and he knew that to be seen in her company and favour would undoubtedly vex her loyal Marquis.

Drusilla had her own reasons for wishing for Webbe's company. Having a rival for her affections would bring the Marquis up to snuff more quickly. Or so she had thought. Everyone she met in London had told her in exhaustive detail how he had never paid any respectable female the least amount of attention since she had left England. One or two had mentioned his muslin dealings, but she dismissed those as mere bachelor's fare.

So she had every expectation of being swept off her feet. And she had predicted airily that she would have a declaration from him within her first week. Instead, all he had given her was the most perfunctory of morning calls, hardly a feat worth boasting about, as her cousin Letitia maliciously pointed out. So much for her prophecy that she could wrap a Marquis about one thumb and a Viscount round the other without even trying.

Clearly the time had come to take a hand in this affair, and her first step was to be seen publicly now with Webbe at her side. She could not avoid a tiny shiver of excitement, wondering what the Marquis might do when he saw her with him. Two men battling over her had always stirred her blood. And nothing would add more to her consequence!

It was a quarter past five when Stanwyck finally appeared on Prince. A collective murmur of appreciation swept through the horse-mad crowd, carefully assessing the rider and mount making their way on the path. The horse was impeccable in step, coat and temperament.

'A capital buy,' Lord Sefton observed to Mr Philip Dudley, who nodded his agreement.

'About the equal of Webbe's, I'd say.'

'Better, in my opinion,' Lord Haverly asserted gruffly when his opinion was sought, an opinion that was shared by some and challenged by others.

Well aware of the stir he was causing, Stanwyck rode briskly along, pausing only to allow a few choice intimates the opportunity for a better look at Prince. The sight of Roxanne and Ben also caused him to pull up.

'First rate, Stanwyck. By heaven, first rate!' Ben crowed his utter delight.

The Marquis smiled at the younger man's enthusiasm. 'I'm glad you approve, Ben. And what say you, Miss Franklin?'

'I know nothing of horses,' she replied calmly, 'so I daren't venture an opinion.'

'Ignorance never stopped anyone from forming some sort of opinion.'

'If you must know, then, I think him a fine-looking creature.'

'A fair assessment of his charms,' Stanwyck drawled. He smiled at her. 'How do you go on at Upper Wimpole Street? I have been meaning to call, but this week has been uncommonly busy.'

His words had been politely voiced, but they struck an odd nerve with Roxanne, as though he had better things to do with his time now that Drusilla was back.

'Pray don't apologise, my lord,' she said stiffly. 'All is well with me. I know you have things to do other than to concern yourself with my stupid affairs.'

Her uncharacteristic coldness struck the Marquis as odd, and even Ben looked askance at her. Before Stanwyck could delve more fully into that, the Major interrupted.

'There's Webbe, Stanwyck.'

The Marquis turned. The smile on his face faded as he saw Webbe's companion, and yet he managed to appear perfectly composed as Drusilla drew up with the Viscount. Not so Roxanne, who wished with all her heart that she was not obliged to witness the encounter between Drusilla and Stanwyck. And yet another part of her oddly yearned to stay and witness everything.

'Good afternoon, Nigel,' Drusilla called out, looking very dashing in a burgundy riding-suit, a new purchase from Bond Street.

'Good afternoon, Drusilla.' He bowed.

'Is that your horse?'

'Yes.'

'Not a bad buy.' Webbe spoke, his quizzing-glass up to his eye. 'A bit thick in the leg, perhaps.'

'If you think that, you're thick—and not in the leg.' Ben hooted.

The Viscount flushed darkly.

'The two horses do look so splendid.' Drusilla volunteered her opinion. 'I can't help wondering how one would choose between them.'

'An impossible task,' Stanwyck agreed.

'I don't know about that,' Webbe said. 'I can think of several ways of determining that. We could, for instance, have a race.'

'That's absurd,' Stanwyck said, irritated by such an idea.

'Oh, Nigel, don't be cross,' Drusilla said. 'I think a race would be a wonderful idea. Say you will do it.'

'Out of the question! It's idiotish.'

She pulled her face into a pretty pout. 'I never knew you before to be such a bag pudding. I vow I would scarcely recognise you any more.'

'Perhaps Stanwyck is just afraid to put his horse to the test,' Webbe said, looking amused.

'Afraid? What an absurdity!' To her own amazement, Roxanne found herself speaking out in the Marquis's defence. Drusilla had not paid her a jot of attention, but now swivelled her eyes round, taking her measure for the first time.

'And who might you be?' she asked coldly.

'A friend of the family,' Ben said succinctly. 'And Roxanne's right. Nigel's not afraid of you or your horse, Webbe.'

'Do you always allow your friends to do your fighting for you?' Webbe asked politely.

The Marquis felt his temper rising. He had borne long enough with Webbe's taunts. And while he did not like being pushed into a match, perhaps by winning it he would silence the Viscount once and for all.

'Prince can hold his own against anyone,' he snapped. 'It's your Arabian I was thinking of. By the by, what did you name him?'

'Aladdin. And don't waste your pity on him. Save it for your own horse. He'll need it if we do race.'

'Oh, Stanwyck, do say you'll race,' Drusilla coaxed. 'Otherwise we'll never know who has the better horse, you or Webbe.'

'Or who is the better rider, you or I,' Webbe added.

'Do it for me,' Drusilla implored.

'Very well,' Stanwyck said, giving in.

Drusilla clapped her hands and gave a squeal of delight. 'Good.'

After fifteen minutes of discussion—in which Mrs Goodheart played a substantial part—the race was finally set to take place Monday morning, two days hence, at ten.

'Would you care to add a friendly wager to the race, Stanwyck?' Webbe drawled. 'Nothing very deep. Perhaps just a thousand pounds.'

Roxanne gasped. Even Drusilla looked amazed at the sum mentioned.

'Lud, Webbe, that is hardly chicken stakes,' she said.

'If Stanwyck finds it too dear...'

'He doesn't,' the Marquis snapped. 'A thousand pounds it is.' He bowed to the ladies and rode off. He did not like to admit it, but he was nettled at having consented to such a preposterous contest. Racing about the Serpentine as though he were a schoolboy! He did not have long to nurse such misgivings, for his cronies were upon him within moments, desiring to know all that had passed between him and Webbe.

Aside from acknowledging the time of the race, he said very little, and it was left to Webbe, ably assisted by Mrs Goodheart, to furnish more details of the competition.

'Bound to be the race of the year,' Ben said to Roxanne as they drove towards the gate. In his excitement, the Major had failed to notice his companion's preoccupied air. 'Monday morning, twice about the Serpentine. I'm backing Stanwyck, that goes without saying. Of course'—he shook his head—'those two horses have nary a hair of difference between them.' He stopped the carriage as he saw Philip Dudley waving to him.

'Have you heard the news, Philip?' he asked.

'About the race? Yes, indeed. I wouldn't have thought Stanwyck would do such a thing. He always used to call such a race sheer exhibitionism. Webbe must have finally driven him to the wall.'

'I think it was Drusilla who did the driving,' Ben said, and then, noticing Philip's quizzical look at Roxanne, hastily performed the introductions.

'Can't see anyone backing Webbe, can you?' Ben asked, returning to the topic dearest to his heart.

Philip shrugged. 'Bound to be some that fancy him. I don't enjoy saying it, but Webbe does have a good seat and quick hands, and his Aladdin is as fast as the wind.'

Ben recoiled at such heresy. 'You don't mean to imply that he'll beat Stanwyck?'

'I hope not. The race is as evenly matched as they come. Perhaps the incentive Drusilla provides will make the difference.'

'Stanwyck always did have a soft spot for her,' the Major agreed.

'This goes a mite further than just wearing his heart on the sleeve for her,' Philip replied. 'Didn't you hear? Drusilla has announced that she will attend Lady Heathcote's ball on the Friday night that follows the race—with the winner. Nigel shall have to win now, shan't he?' he said.

For someone who had been greatly interested in Mrs Goodheart, Roxanne found herself now heartily sick of the name, particularly when it was coupled with Stanwyck's. And she was relieved when they finally returned to Upper Wimpole Street. As soon as Ben left, she strode into her bedchamber and sat down in front of the looking-glass, contrasting her rather sober features with the flashy good looks of one Drusilla Goodheart *née* Crosby.

CHAPTER TWELVE

'MISS ROXANNE, there's a Mr Skittles calling for you,'
Jennie announced the next morning as Roxanne sat absorbed in her paper-cutting. She had amused Ernestine's
children with paper birds and flowers over the years,
and had thought to introduce Lady Bisbane to their
pleasures. Now she pushed the scissors and coloured
papers to one side, hastily brushed off her muslin dress,
and wondered with the liveliest curiosity what her
grandfather's solicitor might want with her.

'Miss Franklin, it is good to see you looking so well,'
Mr Skittles said.

She thought it best to be frank with him. 'Mr Skittles,
be assured that I bear you no animosity. But I must warn
you that if you bear a message or a threat from Grandfather, I shan't stay to listen to it.'

The solicitor's Adam's apple bobbed up and down.
'I'm not surprised that you would think I were here on
behalf of the general,' he said with a wry smile. 'But I
do have other clients. For instance, Lady Langley.'

Roxanne wrinkled her nose. 'Lady Langley?'

He nodded. 'It's on her behalf that I am here. Do you
think we could sit?'

'Yes, of course,' she said, waving him to the Windsor
chair. 'Pray don't think me a perfect wet goose, Mr
Skittles, but who is Lady Langley?'

A ghost of a smile flitted across the solicitor's lips.
'I'm not surprised that you may have forgotten her. Actually, you might have known her as Lady Fogarty. She

141

married Langley only two years ago. A cousin of yours, I believe. On your father's side.'

'If so, a very remote one,' Roxanne observed. 'I never heard Papa mention her name.'

'Not so remote,' Mr Skittles retorted with a smile. 'She left you ten thousand pounds in her will.'

Roxanne had been staring absent-mindedly at the hideous wallpaper behind Mr Skittles's chair, but she now turned her full attention on the solicitor. 'Did you say ten thousand pounds?' she asked, unable to trust her ears.

'Indeed I did.' He beamed happily.

'But you must be jesting!'

'Oh, I never jest when it comes to money, Miss Franklin,' the solicitor said, looking shocked at such a suggestion. 'It wouldn't be at all the thing. Lady Langley died two months ago in Herefordshire. Her will was finally settled this week. She's left you ten thousand pounds, clear and free.'

Roxanne rose from her chair. 'But she scarcely knew me.'

'I believe she had a fondness for your mother. That might account for her leaving the money to you.'

'Could there be an error?' Roxanne asked quickly.

'Oh, no,' Mr Skittles assured her. 'I've checked and double-checked. My father did the same. You are a wealthy young lady now.'

'Am I?' Roxanne asked, bowled over by her sudden change of circumstances. 'How very odd that shall be.'

'You shall become accustomed to it rapidly,' Mr Skittles told her. He took a sheaf of documents out of a coat pocket. 'I brought the papers for you to sign. Once you do so, I'll have the necessary monies transferred to your bank. Mr Child is your banker, is he not?'

'Yes, Child is my banker,' Roxanne agreed, still trying to make head or tail of her new situation. Ten thousand pounds! With it, she could set up a small establishment of her own, live quietly and happily and even provide for Amanda. Or else she could start that school in some quiet part of the country.

Mr Skittles's cough summoned her from her reverie.

'I believe I shall need quill and ink, Miss Franklin.'

'Oh, yes, at once,' Roxanne said, finding the inkwell and a freshly sharpened quill. 'My mind is just awhirl.'

'Quite understandable,' the solicitor said. He pointed a knobby forefinger at the bottom of the page. 'You sign there.'

Still dazed, Roxanne dipped her pen into the ink and signed.

While Roxanne was still reeling from the transformation of herself into a lady of means, Stanwyck stood in his library, wondering how the devil he had ever allowed Webbe to bullock him into this race.

Drusilla, he supposed, had more than a little to do with it. She had practically called him a coward in front of the others, hinting that he no longer possessed the dash he had in his youth. But what had she expected? he asked himself savagely. Five years had gone by. It would be peculiar if he had not changed. But it goaded him to have her think even for a second that he was a pudding-heart.

He scowled as he thought of her with Webbe in the Park yesterday. He would have to put a stop to that. Drusilla ought to have laughed off Webbe's attentions instead of encouraging them. But she had never been the sort to discourage the attention of males, he remem-

bered wryly. It was second nature to her to flirt and play
the prime Beauty, which she still was!

His mouth softened. Drusilla! Thank heaven he was
still single. What if she had returned and he had been
married? That would have been unthinkable! He congratulated himself on his foresight in remaining a
bachelor, and made plans to court her so assiduously
that she would have neither time nor energy to spend on
Webbe. Once they were engaged, he would put a stop
to her dalliance with the Viscount.

Brusquely, Stanwyck gave his head a shake. First
things must come first, and before there could be an
engagement, there must be a courtship. And before the
courtship, it seemed, there was a race to be won.

He sat back in a leather chair, stretched his top boots
out to the fire and began to plot his strategy for the race
on Monday. It would never do to tire Prince, and yet if
he allowed Aladdin too great a lead, he might never make
up the difference. The race was only twice about the
lake.

He was still mulling over whether it were better to go
into the lead at once or to hang back, when his sister
Gwendolyn descended on him.

'Gwendolyn!' he said, coming into the crimson saloon.
'When did you return?'

'Last evening,' she replied, pecking him on the cheek.

'What are you wearing?' he demanded, holding her
off for a better look.

'Don't you like it? It's a new *fraise*. It's supposed to
be all the rage in Paris, or so they say. Beaver fur. And
pray don't lead me off on a tangent. I came back last
evening to find my son packed off in disgrace and my
brother embroiled in an idiotish lark that shall win him
a broken neck!'

'It shan't be so bad,' he said. 'I'm quite addicted to this old neck, you know.'

'Nigel...' She pulled off her leather gloves. 'One would take you for a cake, racing about the lake like an April squire.'

'Oh, I would never race on foot, dear Gwen. Much too fatiguing. It's a horse race.'

'I know that,' she expostulated. 'It's just as bad. What can you be thinking of? As though you didn't have an ounce of sense!'

He smiled. 'If you came here to dissuade me from the race, you're wishing upon stars. A thousand pounds is at stake, not to mention my reputation as a judge of horseflesh. I have a few scores to settle with Webbe. He's done me some mischief of late. Ratafia?' he asked.

She recoiled with horror. 'I could never stomach that vile drink. I'm amazed you have it in your cupboard. I'll take a glass of sherry.'

He poured one for her with a grin.

'What sort of mischief do you mean?' his sister asked.

Briefly he told her about the incident in Lady Montcalm's anteroom. 'But you must swear not to mention a word of this to anyone—not even to Miss Franklin.'

'I am not a paperskull, Nigel. You are certain Webbe was the culprit?'

The Marquis nodded.

'What abominable behaviour! I quite understand your wish to show him up. I've changed my mind,' she declared authoritatively. 'The race is not a stupid lark. You must settle that score, win the thousand pounds and, of course, Drusilla.'

He looked amused. 'Drusilla isn't part of the race.'

'You needn't dissemble with me, Nigel,' Lady Haverly replied. 'Everyone knows that the winner of Monday's race escorts Drusilla to Lady Heathcote's ball on Friday evening. Lady Heathcote told me so not an hour ago in Bond Street. She was in transports at the attention. It shall make her ball *de rigueur* for everyone in good standing.'

'This is the first I've heard of it,' the Marquis stated, looking grim.

Gwen tugged at her *fraise*, which was beautiful but itchy. 'How can that be? Lady Heathcote told me she had despatched an invitation to you a fortnight ago. She's such a high stickler for propriety that she daren't forget to invite you.'

'I'm not speaking of an invitation to the Heathcote affair,' the Marquis said, 'but of Drusilla's role as a prize in the race. I didn't know she was part of the victory.'

'How odd,' Gwen said, observing with keen interest the mild vexation on her brother's handsome face. 'Nearly everyone I spoke with knew of it. I haven't seen Drusilla myself yet, and, speaking of her, you must be cast in alt at her return. Sally Jersey tells me she hasn't changed a whit. Can that be so?'

'She's as beautiful as ever,' he agreed distractedly.

From the abstract look on his face, Lady Haverly deemed it wisest not to pursue the matter of Drusilla. She had led Nigel such an awful dance five years ago and then had had the temerity to refuse his offer. But surely she was not so idiotish as to do the same thing again!

Although afflicted by the liveliest curiosity about the Beauty and her brother, she brought her impromptu visit to a close. Nigel, she thought as she left his residence in Berkeley Square, was looking rather more subdued than she would have expected. But, of course, it was only eleven in the morning!

She continued on her round of morning calls, and when circumstance found her near Upper Wimpole Street later in the day, she impulsively looked in on Miss Franklin.

'Lady Haverly!' Roxanne greeted her elegant visitor. 'How good it is to see you, ma'am.'

'Forgive my bursting in on you like a ramshackle creature,' Gwen said with a sunny smile. 'But Nigel did say you were still in London, and I felt curious to see how you got on.'

'I'm in fine fettle, thanks to him,' Roxanne said, leading her towards a chair. 'Has he told you how helpful and kind he's been to Amanda and me?'

'Nigel is shy about such things, so perhaps you'd better tell me,' Lady Haverly said.

Over a tray of tea-things Roxanne proceeded to do exactly that, and Lady Haverly soon discovered that her brother—who rarely bestirred himself from his customary indolence—had on several occasions during the past fortnight come to the aid and assistance of the Franklins. It was definitely not his usual mode of behaviour. And she puzzled over his possible motives.

'I'm glad that you are here, ma'am,' Roxanne said, passing her a plate of biscuits. 'You may be able to advise me.'

'But of course,' Gwen said, settling herself more comfortably in the chair. 'Ask away. I dare say London ways are perplexing to someone new to the town.'

'How much would the rent for a house such as this one amount to?'

Lady Haverly was astonished. Whatever she had expected in the way of a question, it certainly had not been the cost of rentals in London.

'I haven't a notion,' she said truthfully.

'Oh.' Roxanne looked downcast.

'Is it so important?'

'I suppose not. But I should like to repay your brother for its use.'

'My dear, you must not dream of doing any such thing,' Lady Haverly told her. 'Stanwyck would never countenance taking money from any female.'

'But he must! I don't like being beholden to him. When I think of all those favours he's bestowed on me! He even introduced me to Lady Bisbane.'

Gwendolyn frowned. '*Lady Bisbane?* Isn't she the one increasing? Why on earth would Nigel introduce you to her? She can't be more than eighteen! It would be far more advantageous for you to meet Sally Jersey or Maria Sefton.'

Roxanne laughed at her visitor's incredulity. 'I was searching for a position in some congenial household,' she explained. 'Lady Bisbane had need of a companion after she delivered. Stanwyck bullocked her and her husband into accepting me for the post. That reminds me, I must go over and decline it.'

'Come to your senses, have you?' Lady Haverly asked, eyes twinkling. 'I am in complete agreement. A squawling infant exacts an enormous toll. Bawling babes, even my own, have always put me in mind of frogs!'

Roxanne laughed. 'I don't mind the crying, it's just that I no longer need the position. I inherited some money from a distant cousin. But I do feel a trifle guilty about deserting Lady Bisbane. She seemed in need of a friend.'

Lady Haverly dealt with this problem matter-of-factly.

'Don't give that a thought. I know several amiable young ladies who would leap at the chance to be a companion in such a household.' Her brow knit slightly. 'Pray don't think me inquisitive, but your inheritance is a tidy one?'

Roxanne laughed. 'Ten thousand pounds, ma'am. It may not be much to you, but it is a fortune to me.'

'Ten thousand pounds. Very nice. Very nice!' Lady Haverly agreed. 'Have you thought of the difference it will make in your life?'

'I've thought of nothing else,' Roxanne responded with a smile. 'I vow I could scarcely eat anything yesterday, and sleep was nigh impossible. I even wrote to Grandfather, telling him I shan't be obliged to hang on his sleeve any longer. And I mean to advise Aunt Peg—who is Amanda's guardian—that Amanda can come and live with me now.'

Lady Haverly clucked her tongue and pushed her plate of biscuits to one side. 'Is that all your windfall means to you, child?'

'What else?' Roxanne asked in bewilderment.

Lady Haverly shed all pretense. 'With a fortune in hand, my dear Miss Franklin, you might dwell seriously on the possibilities of marriage.'

'Marriage?' Roxanne was dumbfounded. Lady Haverly looked perfectly serious. 'But whom would I marry?'

'Well, I don't know specifically,' Lady Haverly said hastily. 'I've just returned to London, and I haven't been in the swim for a fortnight. But I dare say I could round up a few eligible *partis* for you. I'm sure with a little assistance you might make quite a splash in the waters of the ton.'

Roxanne nipped such an idea in the bud. 'You are kind to say so, ma'am, but I have cut my wisdoms. I am no longer a girl, and no one has ever paid me more than a passing glance even when I was young and perhaps pretty.'

'That's because you had no one to advise you,' Lady Haverly said doggedly. She ran her eye expertly over Roxanne's face. 'Indeed, your countenance is perfectly satisfactory. You don't have those horrid freckles and spots that plague some females. Your bone-structure is excellent, and your figure suited for the styles now in fashion. Perhaps just a refurbishing of your wardrobe, and a change of hair-style, and, with the proper introductions, who's to say what might not happen?'

CHAPTER THIRTEEN

THE MORNING of the great race dawned at last. Roxanne woke early but scarcely consumed a morsel of breakfast, evidence of an affliction of nerves. But whether this was caused more by the idea of the race between Stanwyck and Webbe or her impending meeting with Lady Laura's toplofty hairdresser slated to follow the race, she could not have said with any certainty. Laura had enthusiastically enlisted in Lady Haverly's campaign to get Roxanne a suitable match.

'There goes our Helen of Troy,' Ben said later at the Park as they sat chatting across their carriages with Philip Dudley. Drusilla, entering the Park dressed in a stunning white riding-habit, drove past in a carriage pulled by a pair of perfectly matched high steppers. The Beauty was the centre of all eyes, and knew it.

'She drives uncommonly well for a female,' Roxanne murmured, half to herself. She was conscious of a little envy.

'She should.' Philip Dudley had turned to her and caught her remark. ''Twas Stanwyck himself who taught her to hold the reins five years ago. And, speaking of her illustrious teacher, here he comes!'

Everyone turned for a look at Stanwyck on Prince.

'That's Nigel—cool as you please.' Philip chuckled, for the Marquis looked as imperturbable as always. He might have been out for a morning jaunt for all the emotion visible on his face.

'And here comes Webbe,' Ben said. The Viscount, riding Aladdin, appeared supremely confident, smiling to friends on the left and right and waving to the crowd.

'Damn popinjay!' Philip scowled. 'Acts as though he's royalty!'

'I don't see Prinny or any of the royal dukes daft enough to race against Stanwyck,' the Major said.

'Not unless they fancy a broken neck,' Dudley agreed. 'Look, blimey! Webbe's offered his hand to Nigel!'

Mr Dudley was not the only one astonished by such a gesture from the Viscount. The Marquis, at the starting line, stared at the hand a full minute before he actually shook it.

Lord Sefton, spilling snuff liberally down his shirt-front, came forward from the throng, having been pressed into service as the starter.

'Now then, my lords, let's have a brief review of the rules.'

'Twice about the lake, first one to cross on the second go round is declared the winner,' Webbe said with aplomb.

Sefton glared. 'Took the words right out of my mouth, Webbe.'

'I was merely trying to be of assistance.'

'Hmph.'

'It seems clear enough,' Stanwyck agreed. 'The area has been cleared? No one to dart into our path?'

'Lud, no! No chance of that occurring,' Lord Sefton declared.

'Then shouldn't we get this race under way?' Webbe asked, drawing on his York tan gloves.

'On the pistol fire, then, my lords,' Sefton said, holding his pistol skyward. 'One, two, three!'

The shot rang out.

Amid a collective roar from the onlookers, the two horses sprang forward, Webbe's slightly in the lead. Stanwyck made no move to take this initial lead away, content to remain a length behind through the first half of the lap. The spectators lining the lake were a blur to him. All his attention was focused on Aladdin's rump, now a yard or so ahead.

Prince handled the first half of the turn beautifully, and was not even breathing heavily as they completed the turn about the Serpentine. At the second lap Webbe glanced over his shoulder, surprised to find Prince now positioned off Aladdin's legs. By the half turn, the two horses were nose to nose. It seemed to some of those watching that Webbe's confident smile had faded into the air.

'Prince and Aladdin are neck and neck,' Ben muttered, resorting to his field-glasses. He was standing in his carriage, wholly oblivious of the danger of toppling off.

'Let me see,' Roxanne said, snatching the glasses from him and nearly strangling him in the process.

The Marquis urged his horse forward now. Prince responded immediately to the brief nudge, unlike Aladdin, who had to contend with the blistering crop administered by an angry Webbe. At the three-quarter turn Prince was the definite leader. The bend loomed, and as the two horses rounded it together, the Viscount deliberately leaned his horse into the path of the Marquis's.

The choice was clear: veer off or face the dangerous possibility of a collision. Stanwyck hesitated not a jot, drawing aside at once. Better to lose the infernal race than to risk crippling himself or Prince. But the near miss and his move to prevent the collision had robbed him of the lead, and the home stretch looked ahead.

'Prince, my boy, we'll have to do some serious riding now,' the Marquis murmured, touching his Arabian ever so slightly on the flanks with his heels. The horse responded immediately to the touch, and the distance between him and Aladdin narrowed inch by inch until—accompanied by a ferocious roar from the spectators and the furious whipping by Webbe of Aladdin—Prince sprang across the line—the winner by a nose.

'Stanwyck did it, by Jove!' Ben stood, waving his hat and jumping for joy in a way that made Roxanne fear that the carriage beneath them would topple. She herself was breathless from cheering the Marquis home.

'Did you see that?' Ben turned to Philip Dudley. 'Twenty yards behind, and he made up the distance. I've never seen the like.'

Philip was equally overcome by the race he had just witnessed. 'Best come from behind I've seen—bar none. Where is Herbert Foxworth? The fellow owes me two hundred pounds.'

'If you see Cartwright, tell him he owes me fifty quid.' Ben chortled as Philip plunged into the crowd.

'Did you enjoy the race, Roxanne?' the Major asked, realising that he had woefully neglected his companion.

Roxanne smiled. 'Oh, yes. It was quite thrilling,' she said, her heart still pounding. 'Ben, I've not been to many races. Tell me, is there always an altercation at the finish?'

The altercation Roxanne referred to was in fact a bumblebroth caused by the Viscount's protest of the race to a bewildered Lord Sefton.

'Stanwyck's animal clipped mine on the turn,' Webbe said stiffly, his face red from the exertions of the match.

'My animal clipped yours?' Stanwyck ejaculated, turning his frigid stare on the viscount. '*You* were the one who deliberately leaned into *me*. I had to draw Prince up and out of the way.'

'I took the precautionary measure to prevent you from doing injury to me.'

'Injury? By God, I'll injure you!' Stanwyck said heatedly.

Seeing these signs of impending violence, Lord Sefton hastily intervened. 'Padwick and Jennings were stationed near that turn,' he told the two men. 'I'll see what they have to say on the matter.' Quickly he beckoned the two other gentlemen over to him, and the three held a vigorous consultation.

While the discussion went on, Stanwyck seethed inwardly. He had won the race fairly, and to have his victory besmirched was unconscionable!

'Sorry, Webbe.' Lord Sefton, puffing a little, had returned. 'Pedwick and Jennings are agreed that it was you who very nearly caused a nasty spill on the turn. Were it not for Stanwyck's quick hands in drawing aside his mount, he might have been pitched under the hooves.'

The Viscount sneered. 'I see you have friends everywhere, Stanwyck,' he snarled and stalked off.

Although vindicated, Stanwyck felt sorely tempted to go after the other man, call him out and settle their differences once and for all. Duelling as a rule went against the grain, but Webbe had played fast and loose with him for the last time.

'Of all the abominable gall,' he muttered.

Lord Sefton made a deprecating sound. 'He took the loss hard, Stanwyck. He's still a bit wet about the ears.'

'He's a bit thick in the head, if you ask me!'

'That, too,' Sefton agreed. 'Don't fall into a pelter over him. Ah, here comes Drusilla. I'd wager you'll be happy to see her.'

Stanwyck managed to put aside his annoyance with Webbe as Drusilla fluttered forward like a beautiful white butterfly, bestowing a kiss on either cheek. Noticing the Viscount standing with his cronies in the distance, Stanwyck could not resist the temptation to twit him and swept Drusilla into his arms, kissing her firmly on the lips.

The gesture was not lost on the recipient, who had never known the Marquis to bestow such tokens of affection willy-nilly, and who emerged from the embrace wearing a particularly delighted smile. Her strategy at bringing Nigel round was definitely working!

'A superb victory, Nigel,' she said now.

He grinned at her. 'Thank you, Drusilla.'

'This means you'll escort me to Lady Heathcote's ball on Friday evening.'

'I look forward to that,' he assured her, kissing her hand.

The Marquis's open signs of affection were not lost on the others in the Park that morning and gave the quizzes food for thought. Stanwyck, everyone knew, had never been the sort to flirt publicly with any lady of Quality.

'Mark my words,' Ben told Laura when he returned to Cavendish Square with Roxanne, 'Stanwyck and Drusilla will be posting the banns soon.'

Two hours later at Cavendish Square, Binton put down her scissors and commanded Roxanne to look in the pier-glass. Roxanne was all but dumbfounded at her reflection. The hairdresser had cut her hair in such a way as to expose her cheeks, neck and jaw. The stylish cut also emphasised her large green eyes.

'I call it the Egyptian,' Binton said authoritatively.

'The Egyptian,' Lady Laura approved. 'Like Cleopatra. It's most becoming, and it's quite unusual.'

Dismay crossed Roxanne's face. 'Oh, dear.'

'I meant it as a compliment, child,' Lady Laura said. 'I've never before realised what striking eyes you have. The colours seem to change in the light. The cut shall become the rage.'

'I hope not,' Roxanne said, more than a trifle daunted by the image in the mirror. Egyptian, did the hairdresser call it? She was no Cleopatra.

'You will be the hit of Lady Heathcote's ball,' Laura said.

Roxanne was not so convinced, but seeing Laura's pleasure, she said nothing of that to her friend. Instead, she returned to Upper Wimpole Street, where she found the general waiting for her.

'Good God, girl, what have you done to yourself?' he thundered when he clapped eyes on her; hardly the type of reaction that would have boosted anyone's self-confidence.

'I've had my hair done,' she said defensively.

'Had it butchered, you mean!' He snorted. 'You look like one of those high-flyers. And what do you mean by living here under the protection of a man?'

Roxanne stripped off her lavender kid gloves and eyed her grandfather. 'I don't think my hair or my behaviour is of any further concern to you, sir,' she said, trying to keep a civil tongue in her head. 'You washed your hands of me and Amanda, if you recall.'

The general scowled. 'I acted hastily. You can't live here alone.'

'You err. I can and have been doing so.'

'It's causing talk.'

'Everything anyone does in London causes talk, Grandfather. If the prattle-boxes didn't have a new topic to tease themselves with, they would be sunk into gloom. And how did you find me anyway?'

'I saw Skittles on a private matter. He told me you had inherited the Langley money. I managed to wheedle the address from him. Is it true about the Langley money?'

Roxanne smiled at him. 'Would there be any reason for your solicitor to lie to you, Grandfather? And, if you must know, yes, Lady Langley was kind enough to remember me in her will. And you cannot accuse me of mischief with that, for I don't even remember what she looked like.'

'Blast it, girl, you've no head for finances! You'll squander it on the Exchange or spend it on fancy dresses,' he said with a meaningful look at her new walking-dress. 'That's why I've decided to forgive you your past excesses. I'll help you to invest the funds. I've several schemes that are sure to multiply that amount.'

'That's civil of you, Grandfather, but no, thank you.'

'Eh, what?' The general looked startled.

'I've refused your kind proposition,' Roxanne said, speaking sweetly. 'Mr Skittles has arranged to have the money transferred to my banker. Mr Child will advise me accordingly.'

'Bankers don't know anything.'

Roxanne felt close to laughing at his conceit. Her grandfather had never been an expert on financial matters himself and had squandered quite a sum in the past on a set of gold tractors, said to cure all manner of ailments and which upon closer examination turned out to be nothing but a ruse.

'Why are you so eager to involve yourself now, Grandfather?' she asked. 'You are not in need of funds yourself, or are you?'

'Yes, thanks to your friend Stanwyck.'

'Stanwyck?' She frowned. 'How did he cause you to be in the suds? Oh, I dare say you betted on the race today. Backed Webbe?'

'I did,' the general said grudgingly. 'But I'm not scorched yet, young lady.'

'Of course not,' Roxanne agreed, not knowing any gentleman who would admit to being scorched, no matter how heavily in debt. 'You have been frank with me, Grandfather. Allow me to be equally frank with you. Up to a year ago, you scarcely knew I existed. You offered me little assistance when Father was ill and dying. You conveniently remembered I existed when it suited you to find a chaperon for Amanda. But no real affection links us. So I hope you won't be too dashed down when I say that I'd much rather go on alone without any help from you.'

'You're a widgeon! I shan't be in London to help if you fall into the briars. I'm posting off to Bath tomorrow.'

'I hope you enjoy yourself. I have friends here who will assist me.'

'Like that fellow Stanwyck, I suppose?' the general asked with a beetling brow. 'You might unthink a few thoughts about him, you silly chit. Now that Drusilla Goodheart is back in town, you don't have a chance in heaven, not that you had much of one before. You can't hold a candle to her beauty!'

Horrid, horrid old man, Roxanne thought a half-hour later as she cut a paper square vengefully with a pair of scissors, quite ruining the design she had been working

on. Odious of him to imply that she was setting her cap
for Stanwyck, which of course she was not. Such an attempt would be futile. He was a top-of-the-trees
Corinthian, born to a position of consequence. She was
a mere nobody. He had not the slightest feeling of affection for her, particularly now that Drusilla was back.

The memory of Drusilla wrapped in his arms at the
end of the race came back into Roxanne's mind, suddenly causing her to throw the scissors about the room
and putting quite a gash in the wallpaper. Next, she flung
herself on her bed and, as contrition, indulged in an
uncharacteristic but hearty fit of the vapours.

CHAPTER FOURTEEN

'OH, MISS,' Jennie's voice broke with emotion as she applied the finishing touches to Roxanne's hair, 'you look splendid, you do!'

Roxanne stared at her image in the looking-glass and patted the tearful servant on the hand, a trifle overcome herself at her transformation. Who would have thought that Fanchon's gown, a masterpiece of orange crêpe in a dazzling Hussar style, would combine so wonderfully well with her Egyptian hairstyle?

'It's like that tale of the ugly duckling,' Jennie said. 'Not that you were ever ugly, miss,' she added hastily.

Roxanne gave a gurgle of laughter. 'I know exactly what you mean, Jennie. I vow I feel like Cinderella myself.' She could not help wondering how many princes there might be at Lady Heathcote's ball.

No transformed pumpkin carried her off to the ball. Instead Lady Laura's elegant town carriage drew up with Laura and the Major within.

'My word, Roxanne,' said Benjamin as he greeted her. 'Look at you! Everything prime about you.'

'Was I such a homely Joan before?' she teased.

'What? No!' He blushed furiously, trying to retrieve the slip. 'I didn't mean to imply such a thing.'

'Why don't you do something useful, Ben,' Laura put in, her own eyes twinkling. 'Such as hand Miss Franklin into the carriage?'

'Yes, to be sure,' Ben said, grateful for something to do. He felt unaccountably flustered by this new Roxanne.

His sister did not blame him a jot. Roxanne was in her best looks tonight, thanks to the concerted efforts of everyone involved. Laura had a vague suspicion that her brother would not be the only gentleman to be bowled over by her new friend.

The Heathcote residence dazzled Roxanne from the first moment she set eyes on its Corinthian pillars and pedimented portico. The interior was very nearly as imposing as its exterior, with huge chandeliers swaying with the weight of a thousand candles. Soft music trailed down the marble stairs, while swallow-tailed gentlemen and elegantly gowned ladies flirted with one another.

Thank heaven for Laura and Benjamin, Roxanne thought, making her way up the stairs. Had it been left to her alone she would have simply stood gaping at the sights and sounds about her. Instead, she managed to control her trembling long enough to shake hands with Lord and Lady Heathcote and to accept Laura's bidding to enter the ballroom.

The gentlemen present that evening bestirred themselves as soon as they saw a new and exotic face. Within minutes Ben found himself entreated to introduce friends to Roxanne. By the end of her first hour she had already stood up with Lord Cribbe, a benevolent soul rising fifty, and Sir Gary Worth, while Captain Dunbarton had reserved one of her future dances. Gwen and Laura meanwhile were busy satisfying the quizzes and circulating the details of Roxanne's history as an eligible heiress new to London.

'Not in the ordinary way,' Lady Jersey said to Lady Sefton. 'A bit of the Egyptian look about her. That comes from the eyes, or is it the hair? I wonder what I shall look like with mine cropped that way?'

'Lud, Sally, no one would recognise you!' Her friend recoiled in the liveliest horror.

'That has its advantages at times. Egypt is so romantic,' she went on. 'I have always had a wish to see the Nile.'

'I would think it would be just the same as the Thames,' Lady Sefton, a practical sort, replied.

'It is not the same at all,' Lady Jersey contradicted. 'No one would think of Cleopatra seducing Mark Antony on the Thames. She did that on the Nile, you know, and that led to the fall of Rome.'

To which Lady Sefton rather sensibly replied that she could not see anyone comparable to Mark Antony in his prime in the Heathcote ballroom, so presumably the British Empire, unlike the Roman, was safe for the time being.

In another corner of the room two other ladies were also deep in conversation, but on matters that had nothing to do with empires.

'Are you enjoying yourself, Roxanne?' Lady Haverly asked.

Roxanne's face was answer enough. Lady Haverly had never before seen her look quite so excited and lovely.

'Everyone has been so kind to me,' Roxanne said. 'Captain Dunbarton asked me to his sister's soirée next week. Sir Gary asked if I might take a turn in the Park with him.'

'Splendid.' Gwen accepted these tributes to her charge with an indulgent smile. 'Now, are you bespoken for supper?'

'Not yet,' Roxanne hesitated. 'But Lord Schyler said something...'

'Heavens, not Schyler! He'll bore you to tears. Ah, Algernon.' She intercepted a tall dandy who was just passing and who turned an attentive if quizzing face their way.

'Miss Franklin, allow me to introduce Mr Algernon Quince. You haven't met Miss Franklin yet, have you, Algie?'

'*The* Miss Franklin?' the dandy intoned, executing a proficient bow. 'Charmed, I'm sure.'

Roxanne, smiling, was gratified by his attention even though she thought him too dandified to take seriously.

'Miss Franklin is beset with a dilemma, Algie,' Lady Haverly divulged.

'A not uncommon affliction.'

'She cannot decide whom to sup with.'

'But that is easily remedied,' Algernon said. 'I shall take her in.' With another smile and bow he swept off.

'I know you meant well, Lady Haverly,' Roxanne said after he had gone, 'but I wish you had not. I have no interest in dandies.' Her face wrinkled involuntarily.

'Don't turn your nose up, child,' Gwen chided. 'Algie wields considerable influence in these parts. Not quite up to Brummell in his prime, but who *is* these days? It shall add enormously to your consequence to be seen with him.'

'Roxanne!' Ben had approached with a different complaint. 'What, pray, does it take to dance with you?'

'Merely a request,' she said. 'You haven't asked me.'

'Yes, but that's because I could hardly get a word in. Everyone else was poking his nose in and demanding to meet you.'

She laughed. 'We'll dance now, if you like,' she told him. When they were on the ballroom floor, she enquired after the orphans.

'They've gone, thank heavens,' he said. 'But I don't want to talk about them.'

'No, of course not. You've had more than enough of them, I'm sure,' she said kindly.

'Roxanne,' he said with a frown, 'we're old friends, aren't we? I mean, I knew you and liked you even when you weren't so pretty? I mean, well, you know what I mean.'

'You were kind to me even when I was a dowd,' Roxanne teased. 'And I appreciated it. I still do.'

'Well, good. Then at least I won't seem like a basket-scrambler. Truth is, I'm not swimming in the lard, as you well know. But I'm not a pauper either. I've enough to support myself comfortably. And I've been meaning to sell out my commission. There's an estate in Kent. It doesn't amount to much yet, but still. Dash it all, we do like each other, don't we?'

'Ben,' she asked, trying to unravel the tortuous threads of his narrative, 'are you making me an offer?'

'Devil take it, of course I am!'

'There is no "of course" about it,' she retorted. 'And thank you very much.'

His eyes lit up. 'Then you will?'

'No,' she said hastily. 'But you are kind to have asked me. And I hope we can always remain friends. Marriage would end that.'

'No, it wouldn't. We like each other.'

'Yes,' she said a little sadly, thinking it a great pity that she did not love Ben, who was amiable and eager to please. That would have made her life much simpler.

'But liking is not love,' she said. 'And I think your offer comes from the excitement of this evening. An impulse. You'll be glad tomorrow morning that I have refused you. Depend on it.'

'Well, at least I was the first to offer for you,' he explained with a grin. 'And I dare say you'll have more offers in the coming weeks.'

'I wonder about that, Ben,' she said softly to herself.

While Roxanne had been declining the Major's offer of matrimony, Drusilla and Stanwyck had arrived at the ball. Their appearance together—so eagerly awaited by their hostess—was a trifle subdued, which led Algie Quince to wonder aloud to his intimates if the pair had come to cuffs in the carriage.

Thanks to certain privileged information, Lady Haverly could have put the dandy to rights. Immediately following the race, the Marquis had taken Drusilla to Rundell's to purchase a gift. Not content with one bauble, she had begged for a second and then a third, which he had indulgently consented to. But when she had asked for a fourth—this one a diamond bracelet of dazzling proportions—he had balked, thinking that she had grown as greedy as Mrs Kinney in her prime.

Drusilla had then stormed out of the shop, saying that if Stanwyck would not buy her the diamond bracelet, she knew the Viscount would.

Webbe, still smarting from his defeat in the race, had been delighted to hear of the stormy scene at Rundell's and had driven at once to the jeweller's to purchase the bracelet. He presented it to Drusilla later in the week— along with a request for her to wear it to Lady Heathcote's ball. The Marquis would show hackles at that, they both knew.

Nigel, of course, was too astute to miss seeing the bracelet on Drusilla's wrist when he called for her, but he chose not to speak of it, confining himself to matters having to do with the dismal weather and the news of Lady Hollingsworth being delivered of twins, a fact that could not interest Drusilla. She finally brought the bracelet to his attention, waving her arm under his nose.

'It's a gift from Webbe,' she said, practically daring him to make an issue of it.

'Is it?' he enquired blandly. 'Very pretty.'

'It is more than pretty!' she ejaculated, shocked. 'It is the most breathtaking piece of jewellery I own.'

'Is it? Then I must say I'm glad you're wearing it and not me. There would be the devil to pay if it broke, wouldn't there?'

'I think it's much more beautiful than those odious necklaces you would foist on me,' she said, and could not resist asking when Rundell's was supposed to have sent them to her.

Her greed annoyed him. He was quite content to let her wheedle whatever she could out of the Viscount, but he was not about to compete with him in buying her jewels.

'I beg your pardon, Drusilla, I misunderstood you. You made plain your dislike of the rubies and sapphires, so I dispensed with them. I had no interest in foisting them on you, as you pointed out moments ago.'

She whitened, already regretting her loose tongue. 'Nigel, you must be funning. The necklaces were mine. I chose them, didn't I? And I have commissioned a new burgundy crêpe for the rubies.'

'Wear the diamond bracelet,' he advised. 'Don't you know? Diamonds go with everything!'

She looked on the verge of unleashing a lightning bolt on his head, and it was perhaps fortunate that his carriage drew up just then at Lady Heathcote's. Still smarting over their *tête-à-tête*, Drusilla greeted their hostess woodenly.

'Thanks to you two, my ball is a success,' Lady Heathcote said.

Drusilla murmured a vague reply, but Stanwyck smiled charmingly and then led his companion into the ballroom. Webbe, who had come early and been waiting, pounced immediately on Drusilla, asking for her first dance. Without so much as a backward look at her escort, Drusilla drifted off.

'A pity that convention says no lady shall dance her first dance with her escort,' Philip Dudley observed to Stanwyck, who smiled at the hit.

'How are you this evening, Philip? Doing the pretty to any new heiresses?'

Dudley laughed. 'There's a new one about, if you care to meet her.'

'No, thank you. I'd much rather seek out my sister. Have you seen her here? She sounded rather mysterious this afternoon.'

'I thought I saw her over there,' Dudley said, and went over to implore Lady Laura to save him from the clutches of a marriage-minded mama headed his way.

Stanwyck sent off on his search and found Gwen almost at once. She was wearing the sapphires. And how the fur would fly when Drusilla saw them, he thought, chuckling to himself. Gwen, he noticed, was not alone. She was enjoying an animated conversation with a strikingly attractive young lady. He frowned, puzzled as to who she might be. He knew most of the Beauties in London. As he came closer, he recognised Roxanne.

'Stanwyck,' Gwen motioned him over. 'I've been wondering when you would arrive, dear brother. Do close your mouth, dear one. One would think you were catching flies. Aren't you going to say good evening to

Miss Franklin? Or is standing with mouth agape the latest craze among the gentlemen?'

The Marquis paid her no attention. His eyes were riveted on Roxanne, taking in every detail of her changed appearance. It was Roxanne, but a much altered one. And why?

'Good evening, Lord Stanwyck,' Roxanne said, a little nervous at the way he was looking her over.

'Miss Franklin.'

'Miss Franklin has been admiring the necklace you gave me, Nigel,' Lady Haverly said to cover the silence that had seemed to befall her companions.

'Yes.' Roxanne roused herself. 'It is so pretty.'

'And Haverly doesn't quite believe me when I told him my brother gave it to me. It is so enlivening to have him a trifle jealous.'

'I shall reassure Thaddeus,' Stanwyck said. 'I didn't know you were acquainted with the Heathcotes, Miss Franklin.'

'I'm not,' she said, her heart beating faster. Never had she seen him in full ball-dress. He looked even more magnificent than usual. 'Lady Haverly was kind enough to procure an invitation for me.'

'Yes,' Gwen interjected. 'And, Nigel, I can't think it was such a pity I lingered so long at Lady Con's festival. Miss Franklin is moving in with me at Mount Street. We were discussing her removal just as you strolled up.'

He frowned. 'Are you dissatisfied with Upper Wimpole Street, ma'am?' he quizzed.

'Don't turn into a regular bear-jaw,' his sister scolded. 'It was *my* notion. We can't have Miss Franklin entertaining her gentlemen friends at Upper Wimpole Street. I've already removed a few of her belongings. The rest will follow.'

The Marquis looked as though he were about to utter a protest when Roxanne was claimed for the waltz by Captain Dunbarton.

'Why do you look so nohow?' his sister asked.

'You take an uncommon interest in Miss Franklin's affairs.'

'It is my maternal instinct,' she retorted. 'Besides, Roxanne needs looking after.'

'I have been doing so since her arrival in London,' he said stiffly.

Lady Haverly fanned herself. 'Don't be an old woman, Nigel. Open your eyes. Just see how Roxanne is being feted and courted tonight. And this is only the beginning. I shouldn't be surprised if she makes a match before the Season ends.'

At the mention of a match, the Marquis's eyes narrowed. 'Do you mean marriage?'

'Of course, dolt!' his sister snapped. 'She's not the type of female one offers carte blanche to. And it's not far-fetched. She is pretty enough, and with her new clothes and hair she looks quite stunning. And she has a fortune now. So who is to say what won't happen?'

His frown deepened. 'What fortune?'

Lady Haverly looked amazed. 'Do you mean to say you don't know? I thought you would be one of the first she would have told, being at first oars with her, the way you say you are.'

'I have been occupied this week,' he said, vexed.

'Well, she has inherited ten thousand pounds from a cousin.'

'Zounds, Gwen, I hope you haven't been addled enough to tell people this?'

'Of course I have,' she said, momentarily confused at being on the defensive. 'It adds to her attractions.'

The Marquis snorted. 'She will attract nothing but fortune-hunters.'

'Don't be absurd! She's not a green girl. And some fortune-hunters are very charming.'

He inhaled a pinch of snuff. 'I see I shall have to help with this charade.'

'Hardly a charade!' his sister countered. 'Miss Franklin is the belle of the ball. There's nothing the least bit of a sham about her.'

'I know. But she'll need help and advice once the fortune-hunters arrive.'

'Since she is your responsibility, you can provide that,' Gwen said with a quizzing look at him. 'You can play at being the father confessor.'

He laughed ruefully. 'I'm not in orders, Gwen.'

'Granted. Then shall we say an older brother? And, speaking of responsibilities, Nigel, have you spoken to Jonathon yet?'

'Jonathon who?' he asked, puzzled.

'Your heir, you gudgeon!' his sister railed. 'I don't know why, out of all the other relations we have, you picked him out, but since you did, it would behove you to remember his name.'

The Marquis was greatly astonished. 'Do you mean Jonathon's back from wherever the devil he was?'

The good Mr Beamish was definitely back and from Boston, as he informed Stanwyck minutes later when they were reunited in the ballroom. The five years of travel had worked a remarkable change in young Jonathon. At the time of his departure from London he had been a pasty-faced young man addicted to overly large neckcloths he could not control. He also had an alarming tendency to trip over his own feet and spill his snuff.

Now at twenty-seven, he seemed self-assured enough to tie a decent Oriental, no doubt a consequence of his travels. He also managed to flick open his snuffbox without any grave mishap, which the Marquis could only count as a favourable omen.

Jonathon was now nearly as tall as Stanwyck, but not as well built, sharing none of the Marquis's addiction to sport. His mother, according to the claims within the family, had a propensity to spoil him. Traces of the family features could be seen in the squarish jaw and the aquiline nose. In some quarters the inevitable comment could be heard that Jonathon was merely a watered-down version of the Marquis, a comment that Jonathon would not have disputed.

'When did you get back?' Stanwyck asked his heir.

'Yesterday. I mean to go down to Buckinghamshire and settle Father's estate. I've been away too long, as is. Everything's a muddle there.'

Stanwyck nodded, recalling that Jonathon's father had left the estate in woeful shape and that it was the threat of having to settle things which might have kept Jonathon away so long. He listened now indulgently to his heir's scheme to refurbish the residence and grounds, a plan which involved a good deal of construction, including a pagoda or two. Jonathon showed a marked leaning toward Mr Campbell's view of gardens rather than Mr Capability Brown's.

'And perhaps a Chinese puzzle garden and fishing pavilion, too,' Jonathon went on. 'The thing is, if I do everything I want, it will cost a fortune. I have some monies that Father left me.'

'My dear Jonathon, you have only to apply to me,' the Marquis protested. 'As my heir, you are entitled to

an allowance, which I shall resume sending as soon as
you can tell me your address.'

'That's generous of you, Nigel.'

'If you plan to stay for any time in London, I'll send
you the money tomorrow. Prices in the past five years
have risen astronomically. I shall send my secretary round
to you. Where are you living?'

'At Green Street. Thank you, Nigel. Is there anything
I can do for you?'

The Marquis laughed. 'If it comes to that, you could
always attempt to find yourself a rich wife,' he said, and
moved off, only to be intercepted by Webbe and Drusilla.

Drusilla felt a little shiver of anticipation.

'I am returning Drusilla to you, Stanwyck, lest you
think I would abscond with the belle of the ball,' Webbe
said.

'Lud, Webbe, you shall turn my head with such talk.
I vow you shall turn me so top-lofty there shan't be any
bearing me. Stanwyck, we must dance.'

Obediently he led her out. As they twirled about the
ballroom, he saw Roxanne partnered with young Trane.
Who would have believed that she could be so beautifully turned out? His glances were frequent enough to
nettle his own partner.

'Is that someone you know, Stanwyck?' Drusilla asked
in an arctic tone.

'Sorry, Dru. It's a friend of the family. Gwen took
her in hand and has worked miracles. I vow I scarcely
recognise her.' He turned his attention back to Drusilla,
but the Beauty was astute enough to make a note about
this friend of the family. And she paid Roxanne the
considerable honour of thinking her a possible rival.
Indeed, as she circulated later amid the other guests,

Drusilla heard more than she wanted to about a certain Miss Franklin.

'Kindness, modesty, and not just ordinary beauty,' Lady Jersey observed. 'Shall we send her vouchers, Maria?'

Lady Sefton acquiesced with a genial nod.

'Oh, Drusilla!' The Patronesses caught sight of Mrs Goodheart. 'Pray, how are things with you?'

Drusilla acknowledged the greeting with a smile, but inwardly she fumed. Just who was this Miss Franklin to cause such talk? Probably just a cit or shabby genteel!

An appeal to her hostess for information, however, gleaned the most unsatisfactory results. Miss Franklin was a grand-daughter of General Franklin. A pity. They were of an eminently respectable lineage.

Drusilla squared her shoulders. She would have to take steps to remind everyone who was the premier Beauty in London now!

CHAPTER FIFTEEN

'ROXANNE, Mrs Goodheart is anxious to meet you again,' Lady Haverly said, her sphinx-like expression belying the warning in her lazy eyes. But she vowed to herself to remain silent and let the chips fall where they might.

'How do you do,' Roxanne said to Drusilla, conscious of the Beauty's scrutinising stare, which made her uncomfortable. She was also acutely aware of just how beautiful Drusilla was. Her face was flawless, her figure generously curved, and she was elegantly gowned in a shimmering gold satin which seemed the exact shade of her hair. And, of course, she could not fail to notice the diamond bracelet.

'How do you do,' Drusilla said, her own scrutiny over and having found nothing remarkable about Roxanne which should have occasioned such a stir. She was no beauty and could not be credited with even prettiness. Passably good-looking, perhaps, if one were inclined to be generous. How absurd to consider her a rival!

'You are General Franklin's grand-daughter, I understand,' she went on.

Roxanne nodded. 'But I would not advise you to tell him you knew me if you chanced to meet.'

'And why not?' Drusilla asked, piqued by the possibility of scandal in the Franklin family.

'We had a mild contretemps,' Roxanne replied. 'Aggravated, so Mr Skittles tells me, by Grandfather losing five hundred pounds on the race earlier in the week.'

'Why should he be angry with you over the race?' Lady Haverly asked, her vow of silence broken.

'He knows of your brother's kindness towards me,' Roxanne told her, 'so he blamed him wrongly for winning. As though Stanwyck had a choice in the matter! There is no understanding Grandfather's reasoning.'

'It is a prime example of the male species,' Gwen agreed. 'Did you wager on the race, Drusilla? I'd be curious to know whom you bet on to win.'

Mrs Goodheart shook her hair, which glittered like starlight. 'How could I possibly?' she asked. 'I vow there's not a ha'penny's difference between Stanwyck and Webbe.'

'Is that what you think?' Roxanne asked, her astonishment plain. 'I find them quite different.'

'How so?' There was a trace of hauteur in Drusilla's voice. She was not accustomed to having her opinions questioned.

'Just different,' Roxanne said mildly, unwilling to enlarge upon her opinion. Luckily, Algernon Quince saved her from further interrogation.

'Time to sup, my dear,' he said, extending one hand. 'I am of the inclination to dine early before the lobster patties are gone. I hope you don't mind.'

'Algie, how like you to be so audacious.' Drusilla laughed as she took his hand. 'Not even a how-do-you-do? Just the announcement that you will take me in to supper? I vow I am tempted to say no, just to teach you a lesson.'

'Beg pardon, my dear,' Algernon said urbanely, slipping his hand from Drusilla's grasp. 'You misunderstand me, I'm afraid, Dru, my pet. I was speaking to Miss Franklin. We had arranged to sup earlier in the evening.'

'I see,' Drusilla said, her cheeks aflame. She was more than a little abashed that the famed dandy should have singled out Roxanne.

She went off in high dudgeon, most displeased by the turn the night was taking. First Stanwyck's wandering attention and now Algernon doing the pretty to a veritable nobody. All that remained to make her defeat complete would be for Webbe to start dangling after the Franklin chit as well.

On this score at least, Drusilla need not have teased herself. The Viscount's attachment to her was sincere, motivated not by any great passion for her but by his intense dislike of Stanwyck. The débâcle of the race behind him, Webbe grew more determined with each day to win Drusilla's hand. The wags at White's had spoken often of Stanwyck finally capturing Drusilla now that she was widowed. Everyone knew that he had lost her once, before and here he had a second chance to realise his life's dream. But they had all reckoned without Webbe.

The race between Aladdin and Prince would be forgotten soon, but snatching Drusilla from under Stanwyck's nose would be a plum to last a lifetime! Now, seeing Drusilla standing by herself, he strolled over.

'All alone, Drusilla? Where is your gallant Marquis? Don't tell me he has deserted you for the mundane pleasures of the card-room.'

Drusilla laughed grimly. 'He's somewhere about. I think he was chatting with Lady Laura and that brother of hers.'

'I own to being famished. Since Stanwyck is derelict in his duty to you, will you allow me the honour?'

Drusilla eyed him speculatively. She had learned a good deal about Webbe during the brief time she had

been back in London. He was rich, his ranking was first-
rate, and he was handsome, too. She felt almost fond
of him at this moment and gave him her hand willingly.
The Viscount, feeling rather optimistic about his chances
of finally applying a crushing facer to the Marquis,
beamed down at her as they went in to sup.

'You're letting that fellow sit in your pocket,' the
Marquis remarked later that evening as they danced.
Webbe had indeed stayed at Drusilla's side most of the
evening, fetching her glasses of refreshment whenever
she owned to a thirst or a fan if the temperature grew
too warm in the room. He had been rewarded for his
devotion by three dances with her.

Drusilla eyed Stanwyck carefully. Was that a note of
jealousy she detected in his voice.

'Henry is showing me how devoted he is.'

'Henry, is it now?' the Marquis quizzed.

'I call you Nigel,' she said defensively.

'So you do, but our acquaintanceship runs five years
or more. I didn't think you had much in common with
a cake like Webbe!'

Drusilla glared. 'Lord Webbe is not a cake. You are
being unspeakably rude. Henry would not speak to me
in such a fashion!'

'I am getting rapidly bored with your bringing his
name into every conversation I have with you.'

'Good!' she said goadingly. 'He is charming, and a
far better escort than you. You haven't spent ten minutes
with me this evening.'

'A mild exaggeration, Drusilla,' he said calmly. 'It is
well known that Webbe and I are at dagger points. It
seemed an unnecessary penance to remain by you while
he hovered about like a dog after a particularly tasty
bone.'

She sniffed. 'If it weren't for him, I'd find this ball excruciatingly boring.'

'I will be happy to take you home.'

'Pray don't exert yourself unduly, Nigel,' she said crushingly. 'Henry will see me home, I'm sure,' and with that she left him standing in the middle of the ballroom. A moment later Webbe bore her triumphantly off towards the exit.

The Marquis, furious at being so deserted, stalked off to the refreshment-room, but Lady Heathcote offered nothing more reviving than some very flat champagne.

'Coming to cuffs with the lovely Drusilla?' Lord Haverly asked his brother-in-law.

The Marquis snorted. 'I am in her black books for not dancing attendance on her. I tried to explain, but she wouldn't listen.'

'Such is the prerogative of her sex,' Haverly said from the comfortable vantage-point of a married man. 'You can make it up to her tomorrow. How is the champagne?'

'Abominable.'

'Heathcote's got some Madeira stashed in the library. You might prevail on him to open it.'

'A good idea. Are you coming?'

'I can't. I have the next dance with Miss Franklin.'

The Marquis was amazed. 'You are dancing with Miss Franklin, Thaddeus?'

'Gwen fully approved, Nigel, I assure you,' Lord Haverly said energetically. 'She's taken quite a liking to your protégée , Miss Franklin. She bullocked me into taking her in with us at Mount Street. Not that I mind it. She's a civil creature. She even has Cartier dangling after her. He's deserted the card-room for the ballroom. And when was the last time he's done that?'

The Marquis frowned. Someone ought to nip Cartier's plan in the bud.

'Would you give me your waltz with Roxanne, Thaddeus?' he enquired. 'I haven't exchanged two words with her, and I have a good deal to say.'

'I suppose you do,' Lord Haverly said drily, not indisposed to making the switch. Roxanne, however, was not so amenable.

'Come now, Miss Franklin,' the Marquis said. 'Anyone would think I had the plague! I assure you I won't step on your lovely shoes.' He gazed down at them as he spoke, prompting a reluctant smile from her.

'After all,' he went on as they made their first turn on the floor together, 'the quizzes have already stigmatised me a bag-pudding for letting Webbe escort Mrs Goodheart home.'

'I hope you are not in her black books,' Roxanne said, wondering how she was supposed to enjoy the dance if he spent it talking about Drusilla.

'I believe I know Dru well enough to predict that I am definitely in them.'

He did not look at all distressed by such a situation, which Roxanne supposed could only mean that he would soon coax the Beauty out of her pet. For some unaccountable reason this vexed her, implying the ease of old friendship.

'Fanchon did a nice piece of work on your gown,' he remarked, complimenting her now.

Her green eyes widened. 'How did you know it was Fanchon? Did Gwen tell you?'

He smiled. 'She didn't need to. I dare say I am as knowledgeable as any female in matters of dress. I pride myself on knowing every modiste in London and their particular style. Fanchon is quite the first order.'

'I suppose you sent your friend, Mrs Kinney, to her?'

He looked amused. 'You err,' he said. 'Fanny has her own whims on matters of fashion. She would never pay me a jot of attention. She was wholly addicted to feathers, which I deplore. They make me sneeze,' he said apologetically. This won no smile from her. 'You seem a trifle out of sorts tonight, Miss Franklin.'

'Do I? If so, pray forgive me. I'm overcome, I suppose, by the honour of standing up with you.'

A frown replaced his usual smile. 'Good heavens, what a coming thing to say! Perhaps that hairdresser took more from you than your hair, or perhaps you've had your head turned by the inanities of some here tonight such as Algie Quince.'

Roxanne had found the dandy's posturing a bit absurd, but she leaped to his defence now.

'I think him a splendid gentleman.'

'A boon fellow,' the Marquis said derisively. 'And what do you mean by letting Cartier dangle after you? I warned you before about him. For all your changed appearance, you are a green girl. And I can't help thinking I preferred you the way you were.'

His words stung. 'You preferred me as I was,' she echoed, 'meaning, I suppose, plain and ugly?'

'I didn't say that.'

'You didn't need to.'

The Marquis felt nettled. So much for the civil approach. 'That's not what I meant, and you know it! You're twisting my words. All I wanted was one dance with you, and see how you fly into the boughs.'

'Then how fortunate for the two of us that the waltz has ended,' she said coldly, and moved away, leaving him alone on the floor for the second time that evening, the object of much curiosity.

'Was there ever such a sex as females,' Stanwyck muttered to himself as he stalked off. First Drusilla flew into a pet, and now Roxanne—who he would have credited with having a head on her shoulders—had turned missish. He had borne enough for one night and headed for the one place where he was certain he would find no dreaded females: White's.

CHAPTER SIXTEEN

THE NEXT morning as Roxanne supervised the removal of her possessions to Mount Street, Amanda suddenly appeared like a bolt from the blue, pleading for a favour from her.

'You want me to do *what*?' Roxanne demanded, when she had heard her cousin's request.

'Apply to Lord Stanwyck for a loan of two thousand pounds,' Amanda said naïvely, moving out of the way of several footmen sent by Lady Haverly to facilitate Roxanne's removal. 'What is going on here, anyway?' she asked. 'And, I say, is that a new hairstyle?'

'Yes, it is called the Egyptian. And I am moving to Lady Haverly's Mount Street residence; that's why things are as they are. You remember her, I should hope?'

'To be sure! She is Stanwyck's sister. And you will ask him for the money, won't you, Roxanne? I wouldn't ask such a thing unless it were urgent.'

'Amanda, my love, don't think I'm not glad to see you, for I am. But your request is out of the question. How would it look if I asked the Marquis for money, whatever the reason? And just why do you need such a sum?'

'Freddie's play,' Amanda said promptly. 'Surely you remember my telling you it was the most promising piece. Signor Fernando himself said it has all the makings of a hit and has agreed for his troupe to perform it. The two thousand pounds is for the rental of the theatre, the costumes and everything. It's frightfully expensive. I don't have the money myself and I can't apply to Grand-father, so I thought you might ask Stanwyck for it. He's rich as Golden Ball, or so they say. He wouldn't miss such a paltry sum.'

'You may give up such a notion,' Roxanne said thickly. 'I wouldn't dare ask him.'

Amanda's face fell.

'But since we last talked I have come into a little windfall.' She quickly explained about Lady Langley's remembrance. 'So I shall give you the two thousand pounds.'

'Not give,' Amanda said. 'It's a loan. I shall pay you back as soon as the show is a hit. Freddie will, too.'

'I'm sure he will,' Roxanne said politely, knowing that the playwright was bound to be as poor as a church mouse. 'I will get Mr Child to draw a cheque for you.'

'Thank you, Roxanne,' Amanda said, hugging her. 'You have been so good to me. Now, I must get back to the rehearsals. And remember me to the Marquis the next time you see him.'

Roxanne choked on a laugh. After last evening, she could not even say with any certainty if she and the Marquis were on speaking terms. Once Amanda had gone, she gazed about the house in Upper Wimpole Street. Mount Street would be more fashionable, but the advantage to Upper Wimpole Street was being under Stanwyck's protection. She felt oddly reluctant to give up this tie to him.

She gave herself a shake. She was being a wet goose. Stanwyck did not care a groat for her. He was still top over tail in love with Drusilla—as anyone could plainly see.

*   *   *

Over at Green Street Mr Stevens was handing Jonathon a cheque from his employer.

'By Jove, this is good of Nigel! I shall have to go over to him at once and thank him.'

'Unfortunately, his lordship is out,' Mr Stevens said. 'Lady Haversham was delivered of a child late last night, or so I understand. Mr Dudley came round to fetch him earlier this morning. Something about a wager they had.'

'But the devil take it, I must show my appreciation somehow! Can't buy him a present, though. The chap has everything. I wouldn't know what to give him.'

Mr Stevens sympathised with the dilemma, but it was left to Lord Haverly, whom Jonathon encountered on the way to Bond Street, to suggest a likely route towards pleasing Nigel.

'Get yourself a new rig,' he barked, pointing his walking-stick at Jonathon's chest. 'The cut of that coat is in sad shape. You're his heir. You can't go about looking like a rapscallion.'

'You're right,' Jonathon said, accepting this rebuke ruefully. 'This isn't the wilds of the Indies. I'll see my tailor at once.'

'Forget your tailor, and make it Weston,' Haverly advised. 'He's Stanwyck's tailor. Where are you bound for now?'

'White's. I hope I'm still welcome. I was a member in good standing.'

'After an absence of five years, who is to say who is welcome,' Haverly grunted. 'I'll go with you. It would be nice for a chance to read the papers in peace and quiet. We're having Miss Franklin move in with us,' he explained, falling into step with Jonathon. 'Gwen is full of plans to marry her off.'

'Who is Miss Franklin?' Jonathon asked, puzzled.

'A protégée of Stanwyck's. Not one of the muslin set, mind,' he said quickly, lest Jonathon get the wrong idea. 'Gwen says he's afraid some fortune-hunter will marry her on the strength of her inheritance. Vexes him beyond belief. He's inclined to look out for her. Be a relief, I dare say, if she marries someone respectable: a gentleman, not just a beau off the street. Someone who will do the right thing by her.'

'Yes, I dare say that would please him,' Jonathon said.

The two men reached White's, and Jonathon left Lord Haverly in the reading-room while he exchanged greetings with several old companions. But Lord Haverly's words remained with him after he had quitted the club for the evening.

So Stanwyck was worried about Miss Franklin's future, was he? And he wished to see her settled with some amiable chap, did he? Stanwyck, Jonathon recalled now, had also advised him at the ball to marry a wealthy lady.

Mr Beamish, disdaining a carriage, walked home to Green Street. He wished he could do Stanwyck a good turn. But what? He walked down the street thinking hard, then came to an abrupt halt. The answer stared him in the face, or rather it would have stared him in the face if he glanced at a pier-glass. He was Stanwyck's heir, of unquestionable respectability. He would repay Stanwyck his many kindnesses over the years by marrying Miss Franklin and taking her off his hands!

After leaving Lady Heathcote's ball, Stanwyck had spent a successful night at the green baize tables of White's. On awakening the next morning, he felt sufficiently restored to do a little fence-mending.

He was making too much of the diamond bracelet
Drusilla had wanted the other day. She was a spoiled
chit, but so were most females. And they all had an in-
satiable weakness for jewellery. Drusilla, however, was
not at Lady Montcalm's residence.

'She is out on an expedition to Richmond Park, I believe, my lord,' Lady Montcalm's butler told Stanwyck.

And no doubt with Webbe, Stanwyck thought idly.
He scrawled a note to her on the back of one of his cards
and left it with the butler. Then he went over to Rundell
and Bridges, purchasing a suitably dazzling diamond
necklace which would match the bracelet from Webbe,
and asked the jeweller to send it to Mrs Goodheart with
his compliments. That gift ought to advance him in
Drusilla's favour.

The purchase at Rundell's completed, he went over to
Hoby's to order another pair of his favourite top boots.
Then he went to Locke's, where he tried on several hats
before reverting to his favoured high-crowned beaver felt.
He had just left Locke's when he remembered Stevens's
request that he look in on his solicitor on a matter to
do with his country seat, a task that took him close to
an hour.

When he emerged from his solicitor's office, he strolled
toward his phaeton. As he did so, his attention was drawn
by a young lady standing in the street, blind to the obvious danger from the passing coaches in her attempt to
call a hack.

'Good Jupiter, what are you doing here?' he
ejaculated.

At the sound of his voice, Roxanne was startled and
nearly lost her balance. She might have toppled into the
path of a passing vehicle had the Marquis not grabbed
her swiftly about the waist and pulled her to one side.

'Be careful, you goose!'

For a moment fright had caused her to shrink back against the comforting strength of his arms, but she abruptly recalled just who was holding her, and pulled away. 'Let me go!' she demanded, struggling against him.

'Gladly,' he said, relinquishing his grip, 'if you'll promise not to dart out into the path of the next coach that happens by. You might have broken your pretty little neck!'

'I only did that because you startled me,' she countered.

An ironic gleam came into his blue eyes. 'What are you doing racketing about the city unattended?'

'I am not unattended,' she said, knowing that to appear in public without a maid must make her look vulgar. 'Jennie is with me. She just popped into one of the shops to have a word with a clerk there. They are sweet on each other.'

'The romantic travails of your maid may be of interest to you, Miss Franklin, but they leave me sadly flat,' the Marquis said acidly. 'You should have better sense than to appear without a maid in London's streets. Where are you going, anyway?'

'To my bank,' she said, not that it was any of his concern.

'Don't be idiotish.'

'I assure you there is nothing idiotish about it. I am bound for Mr Child, as soon as I can find a hack. I just dropped off with Jennie for a session with Fanchon.'

'You are not bound for Mr Child,' the Marquis said.

She found his inability to understand a simple fact infuriating. 'Indeed I *am* going to see him, if only I can find a hack.'

'You can't possibly see Child today,' he said gently, amused by the lightning bolts from her eyes. 'Silly chit, it's Saturday!'

A furious blush rose in her cheeks. Saturday? Of course it was Saturday. She knew that as well as he did. How stupid of her to have forgotten. The banks would be closed.

'I hope it was not an urgent matter,' the Marquis said, not appearing to notice her heightened colour. 'I hope you weren't in need of funds. You can't have wasted the ready so quickly, can you?'

'I don't think so, although Fanchon is wickedly expensive. I dare say Amanda can wait two more days for her two thousand pounds.'

Her words brought a frown to Stanwyck's forehead. 'Two thousand pounds for Amanda? Are you telling me you were bound to Child's to give Amanda two thousand pounds?'

She nodded.

'My dear girl, you are in need of guidance in matters of finance. Let me offer you my assistance.'

'Thank you, no,' she said curtly. 'This lies between Amanda and me.'

'Family matter?' he asked, cocking an eyebrow.

She nodded. 'If you like.'

'Well, I don't like,' he announced. 'I see nothing at all to like in the idea of transferring any sum of money, much less two thousand pounds, to a silly stage-struck chit like Amanda.'

'I don't recall asking your opinion, my lord,' Roxanne said, smarting from his words. 'And you don't even know what it's for.'

'That's correct,' he agreed. 'Pray enlighten me, then.'

She hesitated, knowing that he would find nothing to like about Amanda's scheme. 'It's a business venture,' she said finally. 'Amanda has an opportunity to invest in a promising new play. The money will be just a pittance to what it will bring in.'

The Marquis gave his head a sad shake. 'A play, Miss Franklin? A more hen-witted proposal I can scarcely recall hearing, unless it was the idea Mr Bacon had of a new way of plucking chickens. The idea of young Amanda as a patroness of the arts is incredible! I suppose you've read the play in question or had it acted out for you?'

Roxanne was obliged to admit that she had not.

'And still you'd hand over two thousand pounds?'

'I can afford it,' she said, defensively.

'That's beside the point. It's foolish.'

'And I suppose your bidding so outrageously for that Arabian against Lord Webbe wasn't folly either?'

He looked momentarily discomfited. 'A horse is not a play,' he said lamely. 'You'll just be wasting the ready.'

'It's mine to waste,' she reminded him. 'And I don't know how we wound up on such a tangent. I did not solicit your views on the matter. And now, since Jennie is emerging, you can see that my reputation is safe. She will chaperon me back to Mount Street.'

'I could offer you both a ride in my carriage,' he said, as he watched the maid approach. 'But since you would not accept mere advice from me, I dare say you would turn up your nose at any offer of transport.'

'I would,' she agreed, feeling a pang none the less. Would she never get the chance to ride in his high-perch phaeton which had so dazzled Amanda?

'So I'll leave you just as I found you, Miss Franklin,' he said with an ironic bow, 'calling up a hack so successfully.'

She was still fuming as Jennie approached her.

Ignoring the Marquis's advice, Roxanne took steps the following Monday to transfer the two thousand pounds to Amanda's account. She was still smarting over Stanwyck's autocratic and high-handed behaviour. Why was he so dictatorial? And how curious that she had never noticed such an obvious defect before?

The week passed. True to Lady Haverly's and Lady Laura's predictions, the gentlemen came calling on Roxanne in droves, with invitations to rides, picnics and drives in the Park, not to mention the balls, routs and musicales. Algernon Quince declared her the most charming woman of his acquaintance, a compliment that stirred no little jealousy in other female bosoms.

Captain Dunbarton and Lord Cribbe were also seen to be trying to fix an interest with the comely Miss Franklin. So, too, in his own roundabout way, was Jonathon Beamish. Jonathon had managed in his first week home to visit Mount Street twice, ostensibly to seek Lord Haverly's counsel regarding his father's estate. Haverly had had experience in refurbishing the grounds of Haveril and was willing to lend his ear to Jonathon's many questions.

On the second visit, Jonathon had been introduced to Roxanne and had later pursued this opening at Lady Twayne's musicale. Although he had not conversed with her at great length, Jonathon found her tolerable enough for a female. No Beauty, of course, even though some did find her appealing in an odd way. But on the other hand she was not a homely Joan. There seemed to be no obstacle to his eventually marrying her.

Roxanne formed no real opinion of Jonathon. Indeed, she scarcely noticed him. He did not have the animated address of Quince or the horse-mad aspirations of Cribbe, and, if pressed for an opinion, would have called him undoubtedly a pleasant, though prosy, fellow. He also bore a disconcerting resemblance to Stanwyck. At times, looking at his profile, Roxanne felt her heart skip a beat until he opened his mouth and she realised that he was definitely not the Marquis.

Thus she was utterly flabbergasted when one morning later that week, in Lady Haverly's crimson saloon, Jonathon clasped her hand, sank on one knee, and moaned that she must marry him.

'Mr Beamish,' she protested, wondering if he could be ill, 'you must be jesting. We have known each other only these few days.'

This was not the response that Jonathon had envisioned. He looked up at her. 'My dear Miss Franklin, does a man dying of thirst need a week to recognise a drink of water?'

She was not certain what deserts had to do with matrimony. 'This is all very sudden.'

'Yes, I dare say it is a shock, but a happy one, I hope.'

'Yes, but I repeat, I don't know you!'

'You shall in time,' Jonathon said with a smile. 'Shall we give you a week to decide?' he asked, and then took his leave with a merry wave of the hand.

Roxanne's mind was not so sunny, and she left the drawing-room immediately to seek out Lady Haverly.

'Jonathon has made you an offer?' Lady Haverly's eyebrows flew ceilingward, and she tossed aside the fringe she had been knotting. 'Heavens, I had no idea he had fallen under your spell.'

'He hasn't. I don't recall ever receiving an offer more devoid of feeling!'

'Well, Jonathon does have some expectation, being Stanwyck's heir. Or have you already refused him?'

'He didn't give me the chance. He merely made the offer, told me he would give me a week to make my decision, and ran off. Do you think I ought to accept?'

'My dear, it's not for me to venture any such opinion,' Lady Haverly exclaimed. 'Jonathon is a gentleman. He's Nigel's heir and has a goodly income. He's respectable, and is an amenable sort by nature.'

Roxanne could not be cheered by this image, which brought to her mind a pug at her heels rather than a husband at her side.

'Is there someone else you favour?'

'No, there is no one else,' Roxanne said softly. Lady Haverly gave her a close look but said no more, and Roxanne escaped to her bedchamber to ponder the offer from Jonathon. She did her best to concentrate on him, but the image of Stanwyck and Drusilla flitted disturbingly into her mind whenever she tried to think.

CHAPTER SEVENTEEN

BECAUSE of a brief journey to Buckinghamshire—to set in motion the plans to transform his dowdy country estate into a vision of architectural splendour—Mr Jonathon Beamish had failed to inform the Marquis about his offer to Roxanne until several days after his interview with her at Mount Street.

Realising that he must rectify this slip, Jonathon had called at Berkeley Square, expecting the usual felicitations from the Marquis. Instead, he watched as Stanwyck rose like an incubus from his Etruscan armchair.

'You've gone and offered for whom?' he roared.

The force of Stanwyck's emotion took Jonathon aback. 'Miss Roxanne Franklin,' he said. 'Lord Haverly told me she was a particular friend of yours. She's also an heiress, which is all to the good, for McKensie tells me my estate will use up all available sums.'

'Has Miss Franklin accepted you?' Stanwyck demanded, wishing Jonathon's problems with his landscaping to the devil.

'Not exactly. She told me she'd render a decision in a week. That would be in a few days.'

Stanwyck, staggered by his heir's announcement, brought out a decanter of Madeira. Jonathon offering for Roxanne. Of all the absurdities!

'That's good of you, Stanwyck,' Jonathon said, nodding happily at the tray holding the Madeira. 'Toast to me and all.'

'Eh, what? Oh, yes, to your health and all the rest, Jonathon,' Stanwyck said dispiritedly.

'Thank you.' Jonathon beamed.

The Marquis took a large swallow of the Madeira. 'I didn't know you knew Miss Franklin or that you were of a mind to wed. What put the maggot in your head?'

'You did, sir.' Jonathon put down his glass.

'I, suggest marriage to you? Never!'

'Indeed you did. The night at Lady Heathcote's ball. You said it would please you no end if I found a rich wife. And after Lord Haverly told me how vexed you were by fortune-hunters pursuing Miss Franklin, well, it seemed made to order, if I do say so myself!'

The Marquis stared. Was it possible that his light-hearted comment had been taken in earnest? Jonathon could not be such a gudgeon. But then his heir's powers of intelligence had never been of the first order.

'That's why you offered for Miss Franklin?' he asked.

'I knew you would be pleased about it. But the thing is, she hasn't said yes. I wonder, Nigel, since you are an old friend of hers, would you put in a word for me, if by chance you meet her before Monday?'

The Marquis glanced fondly at his heir. 'I shall be delighted to do my part, Jonathon,' he said, a declaration that led Mr Beamish to announce that the Marquis was a regular trump.

'Was I privy to Jonathon's offer for Roxanne?' Lady Laura's voice rose an octave as she surveyed Stanwyck standing in front of her fireplace. For one whose dress was always impeccable, he looked strangely dishevelled, his hair could have used a brushing, and his cravat was definitely not one of his finer achievements.

'Why should I be privy to it?' Laura went on. 'I've scarcely exchanged two words with Jonathon since his return.'

'Then what about Ben, would he know anything?'

'I hardly think so. He's not an intimate of Jonathon's, but you can ask him yourself. That's his step.'

She called out to her brother who was passing in the hall, and he came in readily enough and was soon put in the picture.

Ben's incredulity matched the Marquis's. 'What a queer pair! Jonathon and Roxanne, you say?'

'Then you didn't know of it beforehand?'

'No reason why I should.' Ben scratched his new beard. 'He's not my heir!'

The Marquis let that pass. 'Well, what does Roxanne intend to do about the offer?'

'Refuse it, I'd think,' Ben said, offering his opinion. 'She refused mine. I don't like to think she'd take Jonathon ahead of me.'

'I didn't know you offered for Roxanne,' Stanwyck said.

'Not exactly the sort of news I'd shout about,' Ben pointed out, 'particularly since she refused me.'

'I am loath to deflate you, dear brother,' Laura interjected, 'but Roxanne might prefer a more sober husband like Jonathon. At least he's not in the habit of cutting up larks.'

'It's out of the question!' the Marquis declared. 'She mustn't marry Jonathon. I forbid it.'

Lady Laura went off in a whoop of laughter. 'Good gracious, Stanwyck, you can't forbid it. Jonathon is your heir, but you know he is of age. You could threaten to cut him off, but that would look nohow. And Roxanne is of age herself, and I don't see her listening to you forbidding the match, do you?'

'No,' he admitted. 'She's got rather mulish of late.'

Lady Laura exchanged a meaningful look with her brother.

'Whom would you rather she wed?' Laura asked. 'Cribbe and Dunbarton are said to be trying to fix their interests.'

'Pair of ne'er-do-wells!'

'Well, what do you want?' she asked acidly. 'You can't wish to see her dwindle into being an old maid.'

'It's not as though she were at her last prayers,' the Marquis said doggedly. 'I don't see the hurry to get her wed.'

'Stanwyck, I believe you're jealous!' Ben exclaimed.

'Bosh!'

The Major gave him a speculative look. 'Methinks the gentleman doth protest too much.'

'And methinks you're bosky,' the Marquis retorted testily. Of course he was not jealous of Jonathon! Miss Franklin was no particular concern of his. But he was not about to see her or Jonathon make a muddle of their lives.

Lady Laura silenced her brother with a stern look, then turned the topic, enquiring how Drusilla fared these days.

'Well enough, I suppose,' the Marquis said brusquely.

'Was it you or Webbe who gave her that dazzling diamond necklace she wore to Lady Julian's musicale?'

'That was me.'

'Well, if you've a mind to bestow trinkets like that, I could do with a new mount,' Ben told the Marquis after Laura had gone off on a round of calls.

The Marquis smiled. 'I tell you what, young Benjamin. If you'll lend your weight to discouraging Miss Franklin from accepting Jonathon, I'll sponsor you in the Four Horse Club. What do you say to that?'

'By Jove, you must want the match scotched,' Ben exclaimed.

The Marquis looked grim. 'I don't care who Jonathon weds—as long as it isn't Miss Franklin. Will you help me?'

To which Benjamin replied that he would help a monkey to get into White's—if it meant being a member in the Four Horse Club.

While the Marquis was engaged in dampening the hopes of his heir, Roxanne herself was receiving an urgent plea for more funds from Amanda, who had gone through the two thousand pounds in only a week.

'It's shocking how expensive things are! Everything costs, and I wouldn't ask, but they are threatening to shut down the production of Freddie's play if certain bills aren't paid. We open on Friday! If you could see your way towards lending me another two thousand pounds.'

Roxanne was aghast. 'Another two thousand! Amanda!'

'I know it sounds like a fortune. Lionel Jacobs, who was playing the leading role, absconded with the strong-box holding the previous two thousand pounds. And the manager of the theatre threatened to put Signor Fernando in gaol unless we paid somehow. And we all scrimped and put our money together and we're still a thousand pounds short.'

'Just a thousand pounds? I thought you asked for two.'

'I did. There are expenses, Roxanne. You'll get everything back, I give you my word. It's so close to the opening, and we can't have an opening if the troupe is in gaol.'

Roxanne thought hard. Amanda's infatuation with Drury Lane appeared to be getting out of hand. She had the money, but once her own expenses were paid there would be precious little left of Lady Langley's legacy. Not that she would need it if she accepted Jonathon's offer. But what was she thinking of? That was outrageous.

'Very well, you may have the two thousand pounds, but that's all. I cannot afford to give you anything more,' she said, going to her desk to write the cheque.

'Oh, Roxanne, thank you.' Amanda threw her arms about her cousin's neck. 'I knew you would help me.'

'And if I hadn't?' Roxanne asked, handing her the cheque.

'Then I would have thrown myself on the mercy of the Marquis,' Amanda said with a merry laugh, and soon departed to tell Freddie that his play would go on as scheduled.

The mention of the Marquis reminded Roxanne that Stanwyck had not called on her since they had met so briefly in the street earlier in the week. She told herself that it was just as well. He was still in her black books. And no doubt he was preoccupied with dangling after Drusilla Goodheart.

Feeling rather gloomy, she reviewed the three offers she had received thus far. Lord Cribbe and Captain Dunbarton had offered for her, as had Jonathon. But she did not regard these offers as very serious. So much for Lady Haverly's plans to launch her. Not that she helped her own cause by coming to cuffs with Stanwyck.

That had probably shocked the staid members of the ton and scared off her more illustrious suitors.

She confided as much to Ben the next morning on a drive to Hampton Court. The Major had suddenly decided that he had been remiss in not showing her the famous maze there. Roxanne was glad for an excuse to be out of doors, and it was always fun to be with Ben. He was so honest and forthright. She could scarcely believe that she had known him for so brief a time.

Ben for his part was mulling over how best to keep his bargain with Stanwyck. One could not very well set about slandering Jonathon right out of nowhere. That was bound to look peculiar. They were relations, after all.

'Ben, are you listening to me?' Roxanne asked with a laugh.

'Oh, I beg your pardon? You were saying...'

'I was wondering just how many musicales the Season shall present us with. I know it is heartless, but after listening to Miss Timball and Miss Donahue play the harp on successive evenings, I vow I shall scream if I have to hear another string plucked.'

The Major laughed. 'Be of good cheer. You can always decline an invitation, you know.'

'It's just the since everyone has been kind enough to include me, I would feel a perfect ingrate to decline. I dare say my reputation already has suffered enough.'

He looked over at her, intrigued. 'How so?'

'That contretemps with Stanwyck,' she said, biting her lip. 'I've learned that his consequence is enormous. Several have hinted that it doesn't pay to be at daggerpoints with him.'

'Pay the quizzes no heed,' Ben told her. 'Stanwyck won't hold such a trifle against you.'

'I'm not worried. He can be as autocratic as he likes. I am one female who doesn't jump when he commands.'

Ben frowned, wondering what she would say if she only knew what Stanwyck was planning to do to the match brewing between herself and Jonathon.

They had entered the gates to Hampton Court, and she accompanied him into the maze, laughing as they blundered into one blind turn after another.

'I do hope we won't be here all night,' she teased.

'No chance of that. There's a fellow above'—he pointed the man out with his cane—'who will direct us. Roxanne, I've heard that Jonathon has made you an offer. Before you accept him, I think you should know a few things.'

'Oh?' She squinted in the sunlight. 'About Jonathon?'

'Yes, he's got a devil of a temper.'

'Really? He certainly seemed like the most placid of fellows. Almost too placid, I would have thought.'

'That's it. Calm on the outside, ready to explode on the inside. He's headstrong, too. When I once suggested we change horses during a journey, he wouldn't, and his mount threw him,' Ben said, neglecting to mention that the two of them had been twelve and fifteen at the time of the incident. 'And that's another thing, the fellow doesn't have much of a seat at all.'

Roxanne listened with growing astonishment to this catalogue of flaws. Ben was usually not the critical type, so she was amazed at all he found to fault Jonathon with. According to the Major, Jonathon was blessed with a bad temper, a poor seat and an exaggerated case of hypochondria. Was it a case of dog in the manger? she wondered. She had refused Ben, and perhaps he did not like to think that she might accept Jonathon.

In addition, Jonathon was Stanwyck's heir, a position that Ben might have envied. As they drove back to London she put these charges to him.

'Ben, are you set against Jonathon because I refused you?' she asked gently.

'Good Jove, no. I'm just trying to help you,' he said doggedly.

'If you are jealous of Jonathon, it's nothing to be ashamed of,' Roxanne said sympathetically.

'Jealous? Of that bobbing-block? He's a coxcomb.'

'He's Stanwyck's heir.'

'That doesn't mean anything,' Ben retorted. 'It's not as though Nigel were in his dotage or on his deathbed. He's as healthy as an ox. And he'll probably pop the question to Drusilla any day and set up his nursery. So you'll see where that shall leave Jonathon. You ought to do us both a favour and refuse Jonathon.'

Roxanne looked up. 'Us? Who besides you would want me to refuse Jonathon?' She watched her companion squirm uncomfortably. 'Were you thinking of you and Stanwyck, Ben? Is Stanwyck behind this?'

'Dash it all, you weren't supposed to know! He doesn't want Jonathon to marry you.'

Roxanne felt her temperature rise. 'I suppose I'm not worthy of his precious heir? We Franklins are every bit as respectable as the Elcots.'

'He didn't say that,' Ben protested quickly.

'He didn't need to. I have cut my wisdoms. What has he told Jonathon?'

'Nothing yet.'

'So he works his way by stealth. And you aid and abet him.'

'But, Roxanne, it's not as though you doted on Jonathon or were going to accept him,' Ben pointed out.

'I thought it goose to guineas that you'd refuse Jonathon. And as for my part in the bargain, perhaps it was low of me, but Stanwyck offered to put my name up for membership in the Four Horse Club. I've wanted to join since I was just a greenhorn,' he finished, flinching under the rebuke in her eyes.

'I don't blame you, Ben,' she said magnanimously. 'You were tempted. And it was Stanwyck who dangled the apple before you—just like Satan did in the Garden of Eden.'

Ben blinked. 'I say, Roxanne, that's coming it too strong. Stanwyck's no devil.'

Roxanne's only response to this was a scornful laugh.

As ill luck would have it, Stanwyck's phaeton stood on the drive outside the Haverly residence when Roxanne returned from her excursion to Hampton Court.

Roxanne sailed into the blue drawing-room, where she assumed Stanwyck would be entertained, to find only Lady Haverly present. 'Isn't Stanwyck here?' she asked, momentarily confused.

Lady Haverly, glad that her guest was so eager to see the Marquis, smiled up happily.

'Nigel is playing a round of billiards with Thaddeus in the billiard-room.'

'How dare he!' she exclaimed.

'I assure you, Roxanne, billiards is quite respectable,' Lady Haverly protested. But Roxanne had already departed for the billiard-room. From the doorway she perceived the elegant Marquis hunched over a ball.

'There you are!' she declared, her voice loud enough to startle him into jostling the cue. The ball, nudged forward, went askew. He glared at her.

'You time your entrances poorly, Miss Franklin. Must you bray like a sheep about to be slaughtered?'

'Are you calling me a sheep now?' Roxanne demanded. 'I might have expected such an uncivil thing from you. And how dare you interfere in my affairs again?'

'I, interfere? Ridiculous!'

She crossed her arms. 'Do you deny sending Ben to me with the purpose of persuading me to decline Jonathon's offer? And tempting him with membership in the Four Horse Club?'

'I say, Nigel, you didn't?' Lord Haverly looked worried. 'You called him cow-handed often enough!'

'We'll smooth the edges off his driving, Thaddeus,' Stanwyck said.

'Can't have him in the club unless he's a top sawyer,' Lord Haverly said, signalling to the Marquis that it was his turn again with the billiards.

'Will you two please stop talking about Ben and listen to me,' Roxanne demanded as the Marquis made quick work of the remaining balls on the table. 'You can't deny, Stanwyck, that you've meddled in my affairs.'

'I certainly do. I was not meddling in your affairs, Miss Franklin, but in the affairs of my heir. That's a far different matter. I would have to be interested in the lady my heir offers for.'

'You don't want me to marry Jonathon,' she said flatly.

'I don't want Jonathon to marry you,' he corrected. 'You would not suit. The notion of the pair of you leg-shackled is the silliest idea I've ever heard.'

Roxanne stiffened. 'I'm so low in station that to receive an offer from your heir is deemed fit only for ridicule?'

'I didn't mean that,' he said at once, laying aside his cue. 'I thought it wisest to point out the folly of the match to you. But I used Ben, well, because we weren't on speaking terms. You know I'm right. If you marry Jonathon, it would be a disaster.'

Roxanne grew angrier and angrier. 'If I am so unsuitable for Jonathon, I wonder whom you would find suitable?'

'I don't know. Some schoolroom miss, perhaps.'

'Hah! I'm afraid I'm not enthralled at being bested by some simpering miss.'

He sighed. 'You are twisting my words.'

'What would you say if I told you I was thinking of accepting Jonathon?'

'Good heavens, you'd be daft!'

His words, frankly uttered, put her into an even greater flame. And she turned away, lest she give in to her impulse and box him on the ears.

Lady Haverly, meanwhile, had trailed into the billiard-room with Benjamin and Jonathon.

'My dear, look who has come calling on you,' she announced.

'Jonathon, my word,' Haverly said. 'We were just speaking of you. That is . . .'

Roxanne crossed the room to Jonathon. 'Mr Beamish, I accept.'

'Accept?' Jonathon asked, confused. 'Accept what?'

'Your offer of marriage,' she said impatiently.

'Oh, that!' His brow cleared. 'Well, good. First rate.' He gave her hand a pat. 'You've made me the happiest man alive.'

Roxanne, seeing Stanwyck's stiffening expression, pulled Jonathon towards her.

'Jonathon,' she hissed in his ear, 'kiss me!'

Always the obedient sort, Mr Beamish bent his head and planted his lips squarely on hers in full view of the others in the drawing-room.

CHAPTER EIGHTEEN

'SILLIEST thing I ever witnessed,' Stanwyck growled later to Benjamin as they went out of the door of the Haverly residence. 'Idiotish chit to accept Jonathon. And you were no help!'

'I did my best, Nigel,' Ben told him. 'I called him a caulker, a cake and a loose screw.'

'Good Jupiter, no wonder she suspected something was in the wind!'

'Does this mean you shan't put my name up for membership in the Four Horse Club?' he asked dejectedly.

Stanwyck gazed over at the Major. 'No, I'll stand you the membership. I'd also like to stand Miss Franklin on her head. Married to Jonathon!' He mounted his phaeton with a snort and drove off, looking so grim that acquaintances who saw him on the way home wondered what had put him out of curl.

One of those he encountered was Drusilla, riding in Webbe's carriage. The Beauty, seeing Stanwyck's phaeton, prepared to engage in a light flirtation sure to spark jealousy in her two swains. But Stanwyck disappointed her. He drove on, scarcely seeing the hand she waved to him. Her cheeks burned. How dared he give her the cut!

'Wasn't that Stanwyck?' Webbe asked idly.

Drusilla affected an uninterested air. 'Was it? I scarcely notice anyone else when I am in your company, Henry.'

The Viscount felt his chest swell with pride. 'Good of you to say so, my dear,' he said, squeezing her hand.

Back at Berkeley Square, Stanwyck flung himself into his book-room looking so uncharacteristically angry that no one dared to utter a word. He sank in an armchair, reviewing the day's preposterous events. Jonathon betrothed to the Franklin chit? It was impossible. She might be of respectable lineage and possessed of a modest fortune, but they would not suit. He knew it. Jonathon was not of her ilk at all. He was a pasty-faced gentleman. She would lead him a cat-and-dog life. She needed someone stronger than that, more able to assume command of the situation, yet willing to dote on her and take commands from her as well. She needed someone like . . . well, like himself!

For a moment the Marquis sat stunned by the direction his own thoughts had taken him in. Was he serious? Or had he gone mad? He could not possibly have fallen in love with Miss Franklin. He was in love with Drusilla.

He shook his head as though to clear it. Preposterous! Roxanne was a mere nobody, for all her being a general's grand-daughter. Pretty enough, but hardly the out-and-outer that he favoured. It was stupid to think of her linked with himself. And yet why did the very image of Roxanne kissing Jonathon a few minutes ago fill him with vexation and, more improbably, envy?

And there was Drusilla to consider. He stretched his legs out to the fire, mulling on the years he had spent wearing the willow for her. His love for her had waned so rapidly. He had supposed at first that it was due to her avaricious nature, but perhaps it was because his heart had already found another to love: Roxanne. And what a slow-top he was not to have realised it until so late in the day!

Drusilla was clever and beautiful, but he did not love her. He had loved an image of her in his youth, and when she returned, he had taken it for granted that his love was still real. But now he knew it was not.

'I love Roxanne,' he said softly. She must not marry Jonathon. He would go to her at once. He rose immediately, then sank back in his chair. No, she was bound to think he was roasting her if he declared he loved her now. He would have to wait, bide his time—and hope that Jonathon did not have the brains to think of an elopement!

Roxanne's emergence in society had given the Season a new topic worthy of discussion. In some quarters she was alleged to be as beautiful as any other female in London, a comment which—when repeated to Drusilla Goodheart—caused considerable gnashing of teeth.

Chief among Mrs Goodheart's champions was Webbe. He took every opportunity to rhapsodise over her eyes, dewy cheeks and tremulous eyelashes, until his audience grew more and more bored. So he adopted a change in strategy, attacking Drusilla's rival, Miss Franklin, as a hoydenish creature, disowned by her grandfather and possessed of no more than passable good looks and the manners of a provincial.

'I for one cannot think how any gentleman could remotely consider her a Beauty,' he said at White's one evening to a group of his cronies.

'Well, Algie Quince says she's the wittiest woman he knows.'

Webbe turned, his quizzing-glass to one eye. 'Algie Quince is a cork-brain. And what passes for wit from his lips is no more than twaddle.'

'I think Miss Franklin quite pretty,' Lord Tymes continued to come to the defence of the lady in question.

'So she is, if you like a woman whose own family has deserted her. I understand the general has another granddaughter, much prettier than Miss Franklin, who has been hidden away. No doubt Miss Franklin fears the rival in the family.'

'I think her very charming,' Lord Tymes insisted.

'I've seen more charm in my horse.'

'Webbe!' Lord Tymes was aghast. He loved a good jest, but the Viscount was treading beyond the bounds of good taste. He cast a wary eye at the entrance to the room, where Stanwyck and Major Bentley were approaching.

'That's enough,' he said in warning, but Webbe was beyond stopping.

'And those die-away airs of hers. It might suit the provincials, but it has no place in our society. I can't believe any right-thinking gentleman would find anything pleasing in Miss Franklin. Why, she's practically an antidote!'

'Careful, Webbe!'

It was too late. The Marquis and Ben had already heard his acid remarks. The Marquis's eyes narrowed into slits at the slander directed against the woman he loved. He would delay no further in meting out his punishment. But before he could fling his glove in Webbe's face, another glove landed there. From Ben. Rather astonished, Stanwyck glanced at the Major, whose ruddy face was several shades darker.

'You shall take back all your slander against Miss Franklin,' Ben said.

'My, my, young Bentley, isn't it? I had no idea you championed Miss Franklin's cause.'

'Take back your lies, Webbe, or else...'

'Or else what? Paddington Green day after tomorrow?' Webbe gibed.

'Yes, if you like!' Ben thrust his jaw out.

'Ben.' The Marquis laid a restraining hand on his friend. 'Come away. I must have a word with you.'

The Major shrugged off his hand. 'Later, Stanwyck. I have business here.'

'Go off with Stanwyck, Ben,' Webbe advised. 'You can cool your head. I shan't take offence.'

'Perhaps you shan't, but I shall,' Ben said hotly. 'And I shall have the pleasure of meeting you at Paddington Green the day after tomorrow at dawn.'

'As you wish. Since it's my choice, I select pistols.'

'Done,' Ben said rigidly and turned on his heel. He was followed by the Marquis and some others.

'Why did you do that, Ben?' Stanwyck demanded when he had taken him off to an empty room.

The Major turned. 'Didn't you hear the despicable things he was saying about Miss Franklin? He can't be allowed to keep saying them.'

'I quite agree, but why did *you* challenge him? I wanted that pleasure!'

Ben looked momentarily abashed. 'Oh, did you? I didn't think that you... well, you can act as my second. If there's anything left of Webbe, you can have it.'

This attitude did not augur well for the pending duel. The Marquis entertained his own doubts about Ben's ability to match the Viscount with a pistol. He did not like to say it to the Major, but Webbe was a good shot.

'Perhaps you'll allow me to take your place?'

But this suggestion only turned Ben more mulish. 'I know you think me a greenhorn, Stanwyck,' he said hotly, 'but I'll fight my own battles and duels, thank you very much.'

'You'll be no help to Miss Franklin wounded. And you're already wounded as it is. That shoulder of yours.'

'It's been healed for weeks,' Ben said impatiently.

'I've seen you wince when it's been jarred.'

'I had expected you to be on my side, Stanwyck,' Ben said hotly.

'I am, I am,' the Marquis assured him and, seeing the anxiety in his friend's eyes, desisted in his comments. Ben was determined to meet Webbe.

'And it's no use hoping Webbe will fire in the air,' Philip Dudley told Stanwyck as they left White's together. 'He's too malicious.'

'I blame myself,' Stanwyck said, jabbing his cane into the cobblestones. 'I heard what Webbe was saying. I should have acted sooner.'

'The hot blood of youth. They are always quicker than we are,' Dudley said. 'By the time he hits middle age, he'll change.'

'If he reaches it.'

These words had a sobering effect on the lighthearted Dudley.

'Look here, Nigel, ain't there something the two of us can do? Maybe if I went to Webbe?'

The Marquis stopped in his tracks. 'Bite your tongue, Philip. Ben would never forgive you. He's not about to grovel, and neither am I. We must put our heads together and come up with an acceptable plan of action. I like Ben. His excesses are those of youth. And he reminds me of myself. I should hate like the devil for anything to happen to him.'

Philip nodded his agreement. 'Not to mention Laura. We can't have anything happen to her brother.'

'Lud, yes. I'd almost forgotten Laura.' He paused at the front step to his residence. 'Come in. Maybe we can dream up a solution to this puzzle.'

Over the Marquis's finest Madeira, the two gentlemen attempted to do just that. Philip's suggestions betrayed a melodramatic tendency, which included the possibility of drugging Webbe, thus letting Ben off the hook.

'How could we drug Webbe?' The Marquis rejected this idea at once. 'He wouldn't let us in his house, and what would we use to drug him?'

'That's easy enough,' Dudley said. 'A sleeping-draught ought to do the trick—or a healthy dose of laudanum.'

The Marquis was astonished. 'I hadn't expected you to be so well versed in such matters, Philip.'

Dudley grinned. 'I once had to hoodwink a friend and take his place. As a wager, of course. Well, the thing is, I drugged him and took his place, and the lady was never any the wiser.'

The Marquis bolted upright. 'That's it, by Jove! You've got it.'

Philip looked dazed. 'Got what?'

'The solution to this mare's nest.'

'Drug Webbe?'

'Not Webbe, but Ben! Now, here's what we must do.'

During the minutes that followed, the Marquis divulged his plan of strategy to his friend. Philip pro-

nounced it as great as any of the melodramas that he
watched at Drury Lane.

They parted at the door, Stanwyck to ready himself,
while Mr Dudley took on the greater burden of their
scheme. According to the plan, he called on Ben the following afternoon, proposing a quiet dinner for the two
of them. Ben was still excited about the impending duel,
but Philip prevailed.

'It shall have to be an early dinner, mind,' Ben said.
'I plan to get a good night's sleep and rise early to face
Webbe.'

'It shall be early, never fear,' Dudley said. 'At my place
at eight?'

Eight was deemed a capital time and Philip left—only
to meet Laura in the drive. Her lovely face wore an
anxious expression.

'Oh, Philip, it's you.'

'Yes, how do you go on, Laura?'

She made no attempt at dissembling with him. 'Badly.
Can't you dissuade Ben from this duel? I've spoken to
him until I've become hoarse. He won't listen to a word
I say.'

'I found him mulish myself. But Ben will come to no
harm.'

Laura looked incredulous. 'Perhaps you believe his
vain boasts, Philip, but I know better. He can't possibly
beat Webbe at pistols. That means I shall be bereft of
a brother.'

'No, you won't,' Philip said, wishing he could divulge
the plan to her but unable to do so. Stanwyck had sworn
him to secrecy. The fewer who knew what they planned
to do, the better. 'Try not to worry,' he said lamely.

She gave a hollow laugh and went into the house, leaving him with the wish that he might do more to comfort her. But he remembered that he *was* preparing to help old Ben and went off to alert his staff for the dinner to come.

Promptly at eight Ben appeared at Philip's quarters, looking more nervous than he had in the morning. Some of his sister's portentous remarks had made an impression on him.

'I know Laura means well,' he divulged over the turtle soup, 'but I'd liefer not have her ringing a peal over my head. Bad enough to think of facing Webbe, without her saying he's the best shot in the kingdom.'

'True enough. And Webbe isn't the best shot; Nigel is. But it's quite normal to have misgivings on the eve of a duel.'

'Did you ever find yourself in a duel, Philip?'

Philip shook his head. 'I am of such a temperament that the thought of rising at dawn is repugnant to me no matter what the offence. I have been delinquent in my training, perhaps. A fault that one could lay at my parents' door for not having produced daughters whose honour I would be obliged to protect.'

Ben laughed.

'Have a little more of the wine,' Philip suggested.

'Thank you, I shall. It's quite good.'

'From Spain,' Philip said, generously pouring it into Ben's glass. Surprisingly, he took none for himself.

By the end of an hour, Ben was feeling the effects of the wine, his eyes appearing a trifle glazed. 'Never felt this way before, when I was in my cups,' he said, rising uncertainly, only to fall back in his chair.

'Come upstairs and lie down.'

'Must go home. Laura shall worry.'

'I shall send a footman with a note to Laura explaining things,' Philip said.

'Oh, well, then. I think I shall just lie down a trifle,' Ben said, rising and staggering against Mr Dudley, who was obliged to lift him in his arms.

He transported the Major into the library, tucked a blanket about him, and then quickly penned two notes to be dispatched. The first, to Stanwyck, was simple and to the point.

> Ben is with me, sound asleep. Good luck on the morrow.

The second, to Laura, was much more difficult to compose. He crumpled several sheets of paper before he was finally pleased with an effort.

> Laura,
>   Pray do not worry. Ben is with me and safe.
>   Your Philip

He scowled, not liking it very much and yet unable to think of anything to add to it. Having satisfied himself that it must do for the moment, he dispatched a footman to deliver the messages. Then he settled himself in a Trafalgar chair for a long night in the company of Major Bentley.

The cluster of gentlemen on Paddington Green were faint shadows in the dim light of pre-dawn. The Viscount and his seconds had toasted their night away full of good cheer, leaving Webbe with the devil of a headache.

'But I can dispatch young Bentley with one hand tied behind me and blindfolded to boot,' he boasted.

His friends cheered his bravado.

The only sign of reproof lay on the face of Dr Sturgis, who, as the surgeon present to stanch the bleeding, had grim experience with this business of duels.

When a coach finally approached, the boisterous men fell silent until it stopped. Then Stanwyck and Dudley came out.

Webbe frowned. 'Where is the good Major?' he called out.

'The Major is indisposed,' Philip reported.

'Turned craven, has he?'

'No, I drugged him.'

The Viscount was taken aback. 'Drugged him? Why the devil...?'

'Ben forgot himself,' Stanwyck said. 'He usurped a position that I rightly claim for myself now, and, as his second, I shall take his place.'

Webbe glared. 'Devil, I didn't propose to duel with you,' he said thickly.

'You should have thought of that before you spoke those words about Miss Franklin,' Stanwyck said stonily. 'I don't forget what disservice you did to me with my nephew Andrew. Or the hoax you pulled at Lady Montcalm's masquerade. Your day of reckoning is upon you, Webbe.'

'I'm fighting Bentley, and he ain't here.'

'Now who has turned craven?' Philip Dudley asked. 'You were quick to seize the advantage on Ben, who cannot hold a candle to you when it comes to wielding a pistol. But when someone of equal ability challenges you, you turn cat in the pan.'

'I haven't,' the Viscount said thickly.

'Perhaps this will do the trick,' Stanwyck said, slapping him across the face with one of his gloves. 'Ben beat me to it, but I did have a mind to do it myself.'

The Viscount whitened. 'By God, if it's a duel you want . . .'

'That is precisely what I have been trying to tell you,' the Marquis said. He stripped off his coat while the Viscount stalked off to tell his friends what had come to pass.

'He's quick, Nigel,' Philip cautioned. 'I know your dislike of killing, but I think you shall have to aim for the heart.'

The Marquis made no reply, but his face was grim as Philip went about the task of examining the duelling pistols.

The Viscount stood in the middle of the green, and the Marquis took his place, back to back.

'Twenty paces then, are we agreed?' Lord Tymes asked.

The two men nodded. As Tymes counted, the two began to march off the paces. At twelve the beads of sweat on the Viscount's forehead were a veritable stream. To fight young Ben was one thing, but Stanwyck was something else entirely. He knew Stanwyck's reputation as a crack shot.

'Thirteen. Fourteen. Fifteen.'

The Marquis looked indifferent, his long stride matching the cadence of the count.

'Sixteen. Seventeen.'

At seventeen, the Viscount came to a decision. At eighteen, he turned ever so slightly.

'Nineteen.'

'Nigel, *look out!*' Philip shouted.

But it was too late. The Viscount, turning prematurely, had fired his shot. It hit the Marquis, but though he staggered from the blow, he had been warned enough to turn slightly. The bullet lodged in his arm instead of his heart.

'Infamous cur!' Philip exclaimed.

'I believe it is my shot now, isn't it?' the Marquis drawled, indifferent to the blood streaming down his arm.

The Viscount, seeing that Stanwyck was still standing, did not wait for the shot to come. He unhesitatingly turned tail and ran off the Green.

CHAPTER NINETEEN

WHILE Dr Sturgis attended to the Marquis—who protested that his wound, despite the flow of blood, was a veritable scratch—Philip returned home to contend with Ben. The Major was dumbfounded to find himself awakening at Dudley's quarters.

'Of all the larks to play on me,' he protested when Dudley explained what had occurred while he had been asleep. 'I vow I could wring your neck, and Stanwyck's as well!'

'You're welcome to wring mine, if you like,' Philip said cheerfully, 'but I wouldn't touch Stanwyck's. The fellow is deuced particular about his cravat being touched. And he's sustained a minor wound during the shooting with Webbe.'

Ben was jolted out of his ill temper. 'Never tell me Webbe wounded him!'

'In the most infamous fashion,' Philip said darkly, relating how the Viscount had attempted to jump the mark. 'I doubt if anyone in polite society will speak to him again.'

Although the Major was delighted that the Viscount had been exposed for the blackguard he was, Ben could not be denied the opportunity to comb Philip's hair for playing the trick on him. He was still scolding him when Mr Dudley set him down at Cavendish Square. The doors at that residence were flung open, and Laura flew out.

Her relief at seeing her brother hale and hearty was written on her pretty face.

'Ben, thank heavens, you're safe,' she said, throwing herself on his chest.

'Yes, I'm all right, thanks to Philip here. He prevented me from taking part in the duel. You ought to throw yourself on his chest instead of mine.'

'I don't quite understand,' Laura said, perplexed by her brother's recalcitrant attitude.

'Let him go,' Philip said with a laugh. 'I shall explain everything to you.'

'Indeed you must,' Laura said, leading him into the blue drawing-room. 'I've been at sixes and sevens since receiving your note. I did try not to worry, but I couldn't think of how you could scotch the duel. But you must've, for Ben is whole, and Webbe, they say, never misses a target.'

He sat her down on a crocodile-legged couch and briefly explained about drugging Ben. Her eyes widened.

'It must seem a drastic business, but we were pressed for a plan,' he explained.

'I don't mind that,' she said with a giggle. 'Had I known how simple it would be, I should have drugged him myself. How clever of you to concoct such a plan.'

'Actually, Stanwyck saw the possibilities. He took Ben's place in the duel, and Webbe, the villain, tried to sneak in an early shot! Luckily his bullet went astray, hitting Nigel on the arm. Then, of course, it was Stanwyck's turn, but before he could pull the trigger, Webbe turned tail and ran. No one shoots a man in the back. And that's the explanation I promised.'

'Oh, Philip, thank you so much,' Laura said, clasping his hands in hers. 'I vow I have not had a moment's rest, although I knew you would do everything in your power. And that was such a comfort to me.'

'Just did what any other fellow would have done in my place,' Dudley protested.

Laura reached across and kissed him gently on the cheek. 'Dear Philip.'

Her gesture and tone of voice surprised him nearly as much as it did her.

'Laura,' he said, amazed, staring into her eyes. 'I say, my dear Laura.'

She toyed shyly with a button on his coat. 'Am I your dear Laura, Philip? I must own that, even with my brother in the most straitened circumstance, I could not help wondering what you meant by signing your missive to me "Your Philip". Are you really my Philip?'

Mr Dudley, long acquainted with the wiles of the most accomplished flirts in London, stared down at the lovely face and swallowed hard. Laura? Lovely, sweet, the best of good friends, Laura? Was it possible after so many years of avowed bachelorhood? He bent his head and kissed her on the lips. Her response left not a doubt to either of them that he would soon be departing from the ranks of the unmarried.

'My word, Laura. My dear!' he said as they drew apart.

'Philip, all this time I thought you wanted an heiress!'

He chuckled. 'Didn't, really. I don't know how that got about. I said it once as a joke, and it took. But it kept me out of parson's mousetrap, until now, that is.' He clasped her close to his chest with the giddy sensation of a man who is hopelessly in love.

*　*　*

In another part of London, another lady sat pondering just how to bring one of her beaux up to scratch. It made little difference to Drusilla whom she married, Stanwyck or Webbe. It was six of one and a half-dozen of the other as far as she was concerned. Thus when Webbe appeared at her doorstep, looking rather more agitated than usual, she welcomed him eagerly.

Drusilla could have had no way of knowing he had been prowling the streets for the past hour, still reeling from the enormity of what had happened at the Green. He had behaved badly, but devil take it, he could not risk losing to Stanwyck at anything and that included losing Drusilla to him.

He gazed at her, conscious that she seemed to look upon him with more favour than usual. After a stammered inanity about the weather, he blurted out his declaration.

'Drusilla, you must know how I feel about you. Would you? Say you will do me the honour of marrying me.'

Drusilla gave a pleased smile. 'Henry, this is very audacious of you. I vow it's not even ten o'clock.'

'I don't care what time it is. Will you say yes?'

'Yes,' she said, agreeably enough, submitting to his kiss and smiling to herself at how quickly she had managed to turn respectable. What would Letitia say when she found out that the august Viscount Webbe had made her an offer?

Webbe was thinking of things other than Drusilla's cousin Letitia. With Drusilla at his side, perhaps he could brazen out what had happened on the Green. Already he turned his mind towards possible explanations for the fact that he had shot early. He could, of course say that he had heard Tymes call out twenty. But no one but a cake would believe that. And, of course, that did not explain the distressing fact that he had run in the face of Stanwyck's gun.

He would take Drusilla on a long honeymoon trip abroad. That ought to dampen the memories of those in London. But before too many had heard of it, he would persuade Drusilla to marry him at once.

Although Philip and Laura had come to a quick agreement concerning their feelings for one another, and Drusilla and Webbe had reached a similar state—albeit along entirely different paths—the same could not be said of Mr Jonathon Beamish and Miss Franklin.

Jonathon actually felt quite pleased with himself these days. He had done exactly what he had set out to do: supply himself with a wife who would lend her fortune towards replenishing his estate. Like most self-absorbed gentlemen, Jonathon failed to notice the signs of growing boredom in those about him, including his betrothed.

Roxanne, meanwhile, was regretting the lapse into idiocy which accounted for her acceptance of Jonathon. Not that he was so very bad. A trifle prosy perhaps, particularly about his dismal estate in Buckinghamshire. But she certainly had no wish to marry him, and would not have said so had it not been for Stanwyck's interference. Only, now, how could she cry off without looking the perfect fool?

She was still mulling over this thorny dilemma as she strolled into Hookham's one morning with Jonathon, who intended to purchase Walter Scott's latest work. Roxanne took the opportunity to search the shelves for something of interest to read.

'The clerk tells me the latest Scott is not to be had,' Jonathon informed Roxanne some minutes later. 'But I have been able to procure some landscaping pamphlets.'

'Oh, have you?' she asked, feigning interest.

'What do you have there?' he asked, spying a book in her hands. 'Tut, tut, my dear Miss Franklin.' He plucked it out of her hands. 'That is Byron. You must know that his name is no longer uttered by anyone respectable. You ought to know that—even if you did live in the provinces.'

Roxanne felt her temperature rising. Was he calling her a provincial now? He who had not set foot in London in nearly five years?

'Byron is quite inappropriate reading for a lady,' Jonathon went on. 'Only think of the scandal he occasioned.'

'I'm going to purchase this,' Roxanne announced.

Jonathon stared. 'Purchase the Byron?'

'Yes.'

Jonathon frowned. 'I believe I have made my views of the poet clear.'

'Indeed you have,' she agreed cordially, 'and that makes me curious as to what decadence might be found in so innocent a volume. You perceive me now practically agog with curiosity. I can scarcely contain my interest,' she said and went off to find a clerk to complete the transaction.

Jonathon did not accept with equanimity this deliberate flouting of his wishes, but he chose to ignore her purchase of the Byron in order to score on another point, her friendship with Major Bentley. The two encountered Ben as they drove away from Hookham's, and Roxanne had given him her customary wave, leading Jonathon to enquire if he were a particular friend of hers.

'Oh, I suppose so,' she said. 'But he is a friend of yours as well as a relation, isn't he?'

'It's quite a different manner entirely. I'm a male,' Jonathon declared crushingly.

She gazed at him uncomprehendingly.

'Must I be blunter?' he asked.

'Indeed you must. For I have no idea about what you are saying,' she told him.

Jonathon looked grim. 'I know that in certain circles it is considered fashionable for married ladies to entertain attachments to gentlemen other than their husbands.'

'They are called *cicisbeos*, I believe.'

He paused. 'Yes. But it would never do for a wife of mine.'

Roxanne gave a mischievous laugh. 'You think Ben is one of my *cicisbeos*?'

'I couldn't fail to see the favour you hold him in.'

'Should I marry anyone, Mr Beamish, I would not take a *cicisbeo*, or two or even three. Is that clear?'

'Perfectly.' He smiled, showing very white teeth. 'I do think a frank airing of opinions is best before a marriage, do you not, Miss Franklin? And I also believe, from what I overheard at Lady Haverly's that you and Stanwyck are on the outs. It's hardly a wise strategy, my dear. Stanwyck is a very important person in London. It wouldn't do to quarrel with him. But perhaps I can mend matters between you two.'

'I hardly think it worth your attention,' she said, unable to contemplate the idea of Jonathon as her emissary.

'Let me be the judge of that,' he said with another superior smile. 'Now, what did you quarrel about?'

'Really, it's not important,' she said, recalling all too vividly the Marquis's words against her alliance with his heir.

'I insist you tell me.'

She lifted a brow. 'It is none of your concern, Mr Beamish.'

'If we are to marry, I can hardly have you at daggers drawn with Stanwyck.'

'It shan't come to that,' she protested.

'I hope not,' he said, his feathers still ruffled by her unwillingness to reveal the reasons for her quarrel with Stanwyck, as well as by her purchase of the Byron. He retreated into a silence which endured all the way back to Mount Street.

'Insufferable, insufferable man,' she declared as soon as Jonathon had driven off.

'Has that odious brother of mine been plaguing you again, Roxanne?' Gwendolyn asked, as Roxanne stormed into her drawing-room. She stopped dead, seeing the smiling faces of Philip Dudley and Lady Laura.

'Oh, I do beg your pardon,' she said, aghast at having been overheard.

'We are all family here,' Lady Haverly said. 'Was that Stanwyck plaguing you again?'

'No, it's his heir. Of all the insufferable men!'

'You speak of your betrothed, Jonathon?' Lady Laura asked.

'Yes. He demanded to know certain things that he had no right to know.'

'Odd. I had no idea he was so inquisitive, did you, Laura?' Gwen asked.

Laura had been resting her head quite comfortably against Philip's shoulder, and she now bestirred herself to give it a gentle shake. 'No, but then I am not thinking too clearly today.' She gave Roxanne a bemused smile. 'Pray forgive me if I seem more shatterbrained than usual. Philip has tendered me an offer, which I have accepted.'

'That is wonderful news!' Roxanne exclaimed, coming over to hug her and to shake Mr Dudley's hand. 'I can't think of a more suitable pairing than the two of you.'

'It's quite obvious—now that they are sitting here in front of us,' Lady Haverly agreed. 'And it quite vexes me beyond belief that no one realised it hitherto. In fact, if it weren't for that duel between Webbe and Stanwyck, none of this would have come to pass.'

Roxanne turned ash white. 'What duel?'

'My dear, haven't you heard?' Lady Haverly asked. 'The quizzes have been speaking of nothing but the duel. But I dare say Jonathon has occupied your time, and, I vow, Haverly got wind of it only an hour ago. They have been keeping mum about it.'

'What did Stanwyck and Webbe have a duel over?' Roxanne demanded.

For just a moment Lady Haverly hesitated, catching sight of Dudley's warning look. She felt certain that Nigel would not wish Miss Franklin to hear Webbe's slanders against her.

'Heavens, I would think any number of things would have set the hostilities off,' she said in her lighthearted way. 'Gentlemen are always coming to cuffs over the turn of a card or the cut of one's waistcoat. Cunningham and Hawthorne nearly had a duel in White's over cravats.

And, heaven knows, Webbe and Stanwyck have been at dagger-points for some time, first with the auction, and then the race—not to mention Drusilla.'

Roxanne felt a tiny pang. Of course Drusilla would play a significant part in the dislike both men felt for each other. There was no reason to search further for a clue to the duel. Obviously the underlying reason would have to be Drusilla.

'Stanwyck's not dead, is he?' she asked.

'Heavens, no!' Lady Haverly sputtered. 'I shouldn't be sitting here so complacently, would I? No, he suffered a minor scratch, wasn't it, Philip?'

Philip nodded. 'Bled like anything, but the doctor says it shouldn't cause him any serious problem.'

'And Webbe? Not dead?'

'No, but so thoroughly scotched he shan't be bothering any of us,' Dudley said, explaining how the duel had ended. Although stunned at the perfidy of the Viscount, Roxanne realised that the Marquis, winning the duel so masterfully, had undoubtedly won Drusilla Goodheart as well.

Lady Laura observed Roxanne's whitening countenance and decided that that was more than enough talk of duels and blood. She turned the topic adroitly to the play they would be attending at Drury Lane, the masterpiece by Amanda's Freddie.

'I am on pins and needles to see the play. She has quite a large role in it, too, doesn't she?'

'So she tells me,' Roxanne said. 'But with Amanda it is always difficult to know how large is large. Will you be attending it?'

'Wouldn't miss it for the world,' Laura agreed. 'Would we, Philip?'

'No, indeed, my dear,' Mr Dudley said indulgently, which would have greatly astonished those friends who had often heard him rail about the idiocies of Drury Lane.

CHAPTER TWENTY

AMONG those taking in the Friday evening performance at Drury Lane was Stanwyck, who had endured a few aggravating days since the duel. His wound, which he had laughed off as a mere trifle, had during Wednesday eve caused a fever and considerable consternation in his household. When summoned, the doctor had diagnosed the problem as an inflammation of the wound, which was re-examined and re-dressed. The Marquis took a mild draught for the fever, which happily subsided by the next morning.

The whole episode, however, left him naggy and out of sorts. As his butler divulged to the rest of the staff, this was only to be expected in one who had always enjoyed robust good health.

Dudley and Bentley came calling on him separately, neither of them suspecting how laid up he was. He received the news of Laura's betrothal to Dudley with the appropriate shock turned to merriment.

'By Jove, you two will suit,' he congratulated his friend as he called for a bottle of champagne from his cellar. 'I never thought I'd see the day you'd turn Benedict.'

Dudley laughed. 'Nor I. I dare say you'll join me soon enough though, won't you?' he asked slyly as Stanwyck poured the champagne.

'I hope so, Philip,' Stanwyck said softly, handing his friend a glass.

'Pop the question to Dru yet?'

'Dru? Whatever for?'

Dudley looked confused. 'You can't be thinking of an elopement, I should hope? Bit havey-cavey at your age!'

'No, I rather thought of St George's, Hanover Square, instead,' the Marquis said with a smile playing about his lips.

'That's what I thought. Dru will make a lovely bride.'

'No doubt, but not mine,' Stanwyck said. 'Word of honour now, Philip, but I'd take Miss Franklin gladly in Dru's place.'

'Miss Franklin?' Dudley sputtered half his champagne down his best waistcoat. 'My word, Nigel, you can't be roasting me, can you? No, I can see by your eyes you're serious. I always knew you to be a good friend of hers. You fought the duel over her, in a way. But, look here, she's as good as betrothed to your heir!'

'As always, you have placed your finger unerringly on the problem, Philip,' Stanwyck said grimly. 'My blockish heir, Jonathon, has offered for her, and she has accepted. Since he's my heir, I can hardly start casting aspersions on him. It's bound to make me look like a gudgeon for having him as my heir.'

'I always thought he was a gudgeon as heirs go,' Mr Dudley said. 'Oh, he means well, but he has the talent for putting his foot in his mouth. You shan't have trouble cutting him out if you put your mind to it. It stands to reason—no sensible female would take Jonathon when she could have you!'

These words restored some of Stanwyck's optimism, but the precise method of how to cut out Jonathon still absorbed him throughout Ben's visit, which followed on the heels of Mr Dudley's. The Major had still not forgiven the Marquis for the trick he had played on him, but he felt a slight pang of guilt at his bandaged arm.

'Don't you turn into a quack,' Stanwyck told him sternly. 'I have better things to talk about than my arm. I heard from Thaddeus. The vote is in. Your membership in the Four Horse Club has been approved. Ain't you going to say something?' he asked, as Ben made an inarticulate gurgle.

'Stanwyck, that's good of you!'

'Mind you don't turn over the carriage on your first outing with the club.'

'I shan't, I promise,' Ben said. 'Wait until I tell Andrew. How green he shall be. I'll have to write to him tonight.'

'Save your ink. You can tell him yourself. Thaddeus has relented. Andrew is to be back by the end of the week.'

'Famous. I vow I'm in your debt considerably, Stanwyck. What can I do to repay you?'

'Well, if you must, why don't you come with me to Drury Lane tonight so that we can see Amanda's play?'

So it was that the Marquis made his entrance into his box on Friday evening accompanied by Ben, Lady Laura and Mr Dudley—who had hoped for a more intimate twosome. However, Dudley's carriage had suffered a mishap and was undergoing repairs, and Laura had prevailed on Ben to take them. They were a trifle late getting there and, because of the usual horde of people milling about, Stanwyck was unable to determine if Roxanne was present.

Roxanne was indeed present—with Jonathon, who had insisted on accompanying her for the evening, even though she could have gone just as well with Lord and

Lady Haverly. Jonathon, however, had been insistent, and she had given in. As she watched the guests streaming in, she found herself wondering if Stanwyck would make an appearance. Amanda had told her that she had sent him an invitation, and she only hoped that Amanda would not be too disappointed at his absence. He was still injured.

'What is the play about?' Jonathon's query interrupted her thinking.

'Amanda gave me only the barest of sketches,' she said now. 'It's an adaptation of an Italian folk story about a farm lad who falls in love with a princess. Her father disapproves, which leads to an attempted elopement. That fails, too. Amanda was a trifle vague about the climax. She didn't wish to spoil it for us.'

Jonathon grunted. He seemed to be doing a good deal of that of late, Roxanne thought, and she had the greatest fear that he would soon turn into a crotchety, growly sort of gentleman, forever complaining about the weather, or the food, or the condition of their household. She sighed.

'Did you say something?' he asked, looking up.

'No.'

'Roxanne, dear,' a voice called out, and she spied Lady Laura in a box nearby waving at her.

She started to wave back, but a disapproving frown from Jonathon curtailed that impulsive move. She contented herself with a smile instead.

'Laura might try for a little conduct,' Jonathon sniffed. 'I wonder that her brother doesn't take her to task.'

'Perhaps he sees nothing wrong in her conduct,' Roxanne retorted, taking up the cudgels in her friend's behalf. In addition to being a slow-top, Jonathon *would* have to be top-lofty.

'No gentleman could enjoy such a hoydenish spectacle.'

'You err.' A voice spoke from behind them. 'Some gentlemen do enjoy exactly that,' Stanwyck said, stepping into the box.

'Good evening, Nigel,' Jonathon said.

'Jonathon. Miss Franklin, your most obedient.' He took her hand and bowed over it, much to her surprise.

'Good evening, Lord Stanwyck,' Roxanne murmured, noticing how his coat fitted imperfectly over his arm, no doubt a consequence of his wound from the duel.

'Stanwyck, I'm glad to have a moment with you. Miss Franklin has something particular to say to you.'

'Indeed?' the Marquis asked, gazing at Roxanne, who appeared dumbfounded by Jonathon's words.

'I'm afraid I don't understand,' she stammered.

'You were going to apologise to Stanwyck, my dear, the next time you met him,' Jonathon prompted.

'Apologise?' Roxanne demanded, looking nearly as red as her rose-coloured silk.

The Marquis stared with pointed interest at his heir. Was Jonathon seriously anticipating that Roxanne would apologise to him?

'Miss Franklin and I discussed this earlier, Nigel,' Jonathon said, appearing oblivious of the expressions on both of his companions. 'She deeply regrets her latest quarrel with you.'

'Does she?' Stanwyck asked, gazing at Roxanne, who looked as though she had swallowed her tongue.

'And she is quite willing to acknowledge her error now,' Jonathon said with a smile.

'How much in error, only she and I must know,' Stanwyck drawled, recalling Roxanne's reaction to his assertion that Jonathon and she would be impossibly suited. His eyes met hers now. 'I accept your apology, Miss Franklin,' he said ironically.

'Your lordship is too kind,' she answered in the same tone.

Jonathon beamed. 'There, you see how easy it was to mend matters between you!'

What his betrothed might have said to this was left up in the air, for the curtain rang up and the Marquis retreated to his own box, his shoulders shaking.

From what Amanda had told her, Roxanne had assumed they were to view a tragedy much like Mr Shakespeare's star-crossed Romeo and Juliet. But the guffaws that emanated from the audience made that unlikely. However, it could not really be a comedy, could it, since it dealt with the eventual demise of the couple?

'What is this muddle?' Jonathon asked as the curtain fell on the first act.

'You mustn't be too hasty,' Roxanne protested. 'There are still two acts to go.'

'One was more than enough for me,' Jonathon replied.

A foray into Lord Haverly's box in the interval was not a great success. The usually optimistic Lady Haverly was hard put to find something to say that did not smack of out-and-out prevarication.

The second act proved to be even more muddled than the first, and catcalls replaced the guffaws. The third act was not allowed to go on.

'That was the worst play I've ever seen,' Jonathon said as he walked down the stairs with Roxanne.

'It was horrid, wasn't it?' Stanwyck said, over-hearing, and possessing no qualms about butting in. 'I must agree it was bad, but as for the worst I've seen...I shall have to think a minute.'

'Do stop talking about how horrid it was,' Roxanne pleaded. 'Poor Amanda and poor Mr Devens! How shattered they must be.'

'I suppose you regret your loan of two thousand pounds to Amanda now,' Stanwyck said to Roxanne as Jonathon went off to locate his vehicle.

'I regret my loss of four thousand pounds even more,' Roxanne said ruefully.

'Four thousand pounds!' Stanwyck exclaimed with a piercing look. 'My dear Miss Franklin, say you didn't?'

'I'm afraid I did.'

'You'll not see a penny of it again.'

'Did I hear you correctly?' Jonathon had returned in time to overhear a portion of her conversation with the Marquis. 'Did you say you lost four thousand pounds to your cousin?'

'Yes, Jonathon, and pray don't plague me about it. The deed is done. There is nothing I can do about it now.'

While this might be true, it did not stop Jonathon from ringing a peal over her about the sheer folly of throwing good money after bad, a topic that absorbed him during their return to Mount Street. She could not escape him fast enough.

The night being so young, Jonathon headed for White's, where he was not surprised to find the Marquis.

'Have some claret,' Stanwyck suggested to his heir. 'It's sound enough. I vouch for it.'

'Thank you, I shall,' Jonathon said. 'It's been a devil of an evening.'

'Not a theatre-lover, are you, Jonathon?'

'By Jupiter, no. What a mull.'

'You seem oddly perplexed,' Stanwyck observed as his heir downed two quick glasses of claret. 'I agree the play was abysmal, but that's no reason to look so Friday-faced!'

'You heard Miss Franklin yourself, Stanwyck,' Jonathon protested. 'She's lost four thousand pounds because of that play. That's four thousand less she'll bring into our marriage. She's not a rich heiress at all!' he said, looking aggrieved.

The Marquis poured Jonathon another glass of claret.

'Heiresses ought to stay heiresses,' Jonathon went on. 'Especially since I've a mind to refurbish my estate, as you know. And such things cost. That's why I was disposed to offer for her in the first place. But it seems she's squandered most of her fortune on her cousin. And there are the bills she must pay. I shouldn't be surprised if in the end she has only a paltry thousand left.'

'I shouldn't be surprised either,' the Marquis said. 'But you forget there could be an even worse situation.'

'I doubt it.'

'She or her family might have debts that you would be duty bound to settle,' the Marquis told him.

Jonathon looked up, stricken to the core. 'Heavens, does she?'

'Happily no. But her grandfather, the General, has been in dun territory for years. It's not exactly your

notion of a suitable match, is it?' he asked
sympathetically.

Jonathon laughed bitterly.

'But buck up, lad, you can always cry off.'

'Cry off?' This notion had evidently not occurred to
Jonathon.

'Do you wish to marry a pauper?'

He recoiled. 'But I'm betrothed to her.'

'I can change that for you if you wish, tomorrow.'

'Oughtn't I do it myself?'

'Ordinarily yes,' the Marquis agreed. 'But this time I
insist on doing it for you. You have no idea of the scenes
females are prone to indulge in when they have been
balked. It's better for you to be as far away as possible.
You might think about another trip to Buckinghamshire.
In the meantime, why don't you have a chat with
Dudley? I'll be bound he knows one or two heiresses
that will suit your fancy. Philip?' he called out to his
friend. 'Jonathon would like a word with you.'

CHAPTER TWENTY-ONE

'It was so unfair,' Amanda complained bitterly the next morning to Roxanne in Lady Haverly's drawing-room. 'They didn't even give us a chance to finish Freddie's play.'

'I know, but perhaps another time...'

'Signor Fernando says the play is dead in London,' Amanda said mournfully. 'But that's not true on the Continent, Roxanne. So if you would be willing...?'

'The answer to that is no, Amanda,' Roxanne said at once.

'You don't even know what I want to ask.'

'You want another two or three thousand pounds.'

'It is only a loan.'

Roxanne shook her head. Amanda was hopeless. 'My dear, I dare say this may shock you, but I haven't much left to fly with.'

'Aunt Langley's windfall,' Amanda protested.

'Half of that has gone to expenses, and most of the remainder given to you,' Roxanne said gently.

'Oh, Roxanne, I am sorry,' Amanda said, looking stricken. 'I had no idea it was so bad. Of course it's not the end of the world. You are marrying Mr Beamish. I'm sorry I didn't get a chance to meet him properly last night.'

'Actually,' Roxanne confessed, 'I don't think I shall be marrying Jonathon.'

'Why not? Is there some other?'

Roxanne frowned. 'Some other what?'

'Some other suitor,' Amanda said, 'like Stanwyck, perhaps?'

'Good heavens, no,' Roxanne exclaimed. 'The notions you come up with!'

'Then what about Cribbe or Captain Dunbarton?' Amanda asked.

'No,' Roxanne said. She was not about to take either of those two suitors. Perhaps, she thought dourly, she was doomed to be an ape leader, for without a substantial dowry, it would be difficult to marry. She nursed no illusions about her own beauty being enough to entice any suitable gentleman.

Indeed, during the night, she had become reconciled once again to acting as companion to Lady Bisbane. Perhaps in time she might grow accustomed to such a life, and if not—she made a wry face—there was always Ernestine to return to.

Lady Haverly brought an end to her introspection by bursting into the parlour, waving a copy of the newest issue of the *Gazette*.

'Roxanne, the strangest thing has happened! Look in the marriage announcements,' Lady Haverly demanded, holding one hand to her heaving bosom and breathing heavily.

Amanda riffled through the pages of the journal. 'What is it I'm supposed to find?' she asked naïvely.

Lady Haverly sank into a chair. 'Drusilla. Married. I vow I never heard the notion voiced. Stanwyck, good heavens!'

'Drusilla has married Stanwyck,' Roxanne said in a voice devoid of all emotion.

Lady Haverly had recourse to her hartshorn and gave her head an emphatic shake. 'No, no. Look again.' She flapped a hand. 'It's Webbe. She's taken Webbe.'

'She has?' Roxanne exclaimed, snatching the paper from Amanda.

'It's all there in the column,' Gwen said. 'What can it mean? I know she looked nohow the other week, but to have chosen Webbe! Especially after that dastardly way he wounded Nigel! And look, they haven't even waited. It's an elopement to Gretna. Well, it's certain they shan't show their faces in London for a considerable time. And I for one am not deceived by their being married by special licence or their honeymooning on the Continent, as it says here. They want us to forget about the duel with Nigel.'

A wild hope had been unleashed in Roxanne's breast. 'I wouldn't have believed it,' she said softly.

'I know. To have chosen Webbe over Nigel.' Lady Haverly wrung her hands. 'I just hope Nigel isn't too cast down. This is the second time she has preferred another to him.'

'Maybe it's a mistake.' Amanda spoke up.

'No. They wouldn't print it if it weren't true. I just wonder if Nigel has seen it yet,' his sister fretted.

Owing to dashing about like a madman, the Marquis had not yet seen this morning's *Gazette*. He had risen later than usual and spent longer at his toilette than anyone could remember, crushing one cravat after another. Such signs of nervousness were not typical, and his valet ventured to ask if anything were wrong.

'We shall see in an hour's time,' the Marquis said grimly, putting his hat on his head and marching down the stairs. The first person he saw after his carriage drew up at Mount Street was his sister, who ushered him into her drawing-room with much fluttering and discreet enquiries about his health. She cooed and clucked so much that she put him out of patience. Finally he demanded to know why she was acting so missishly.

'Now, Nigel, there's no reason to flare up, though you have reason to feel testy today.'

'Why should I feel testy?'

'Have you glanced at the *Gazette*?'

'No,' he snapped. 'I don't read it until after noon. Why? Is there something of particular interest in it?'

Lady Haverly clutched her brother's hand. 'Nigel, whatever happens, you must be strong. What do the French say? *Que sera sera.* Or is that the Italians?' she asked distractedly.

'I never knew you to be an admirer of either the French or the Italians, Gwen.'

'Just promise not to wear the willow again. I vow I couldn't bear it.'

Stanwyck had been listening with some impatience to his sister's prattle, but now his face hardened. 'What do you mean?' he asked coldly.

Lady Haverly pressed his hand. 'I am so sorry, Nigel. I know you had such hopes of late. And I was happy for you after the way Drusilla treated you so badly years ago, and now to have the same thing happen again.'

Stanwyck brushed aside her hand and rose. 'I suppose that announcement is in the *Gazette*?' he asked dully.

She nodded.

'Devil. I thought I'd scotched the match.'

'It's a *fait accompli*.'

The Marquis swore long and eloquently. His sister did not chide him a bit.

'Who has she taken? Ben, I wonder?'

'Ben?' Gwen was taken aback. 'Don't be a gudgeon. He's a pauper.'

'I suppose she would need a very rich husband. Well, if not Ben, who? Cribbe? Dunbarton?'

Lady Haverly stared quizzically at her brother. 'Heavens, no. How oddly you speak, Nigel. It's Webbe, of course.'

'Webbe?' He had been striding across her Wilton carpet, but now he turned. 'That's impossible!'

'Look for yourself.' Gwen waved the paper at him. 'I vow I could cry myself for what Drusilla has done to you again. I know how much you wanted to marry her.'

'Drusilla?' the Marquis exclaimed. 'And Webbe, did you say? Gwen, have you been prattling to me of Drusilla all this time?'

Lady Haverly's confusion mounted. 'Yes, of course. And really perhaps in time you shall come to see that it's best you didn't win her.'

'It shan't take any time. I know that I am better off without Drusilla. I don't care a straw about her.'

'You don't?' Lady Haverly recoiled. 'Then who?'

He decided he had wasted enough time with his sister. 'Where is Miss Franklin, Gwen?'

'Do you mean Roxanne? She's in the small parlour with Amanda.' The light dawned at last. 'Do you mean it's Roxanne, Nigel?'

He left her with her question still unanswered and hurried into the small parlour. He found Amanda there alone.

'Where's your cousin?' he asked.

'Upstairs. She wanted to show me a book of poems she had bought,' Amanda said, taking his unorthodox greeting in her stride. 'She'll be down shortly, I'm sure.'

'Good.' He paced for a moment.

'Lord Stanwyck, would you do me a favour?'

'That depends, brat.'

'Lend me four thousand pounds.'

'To squander on another silly play? I'll do no such thing.'

'The play wasn't silly, and I wouldn't squander it,' Amanda said hotly. She sobered. 'I'd like to repay Roxanne the money I borrowed. She doesn't wish to marry Mr Beamish, and because she has no dowry, I doubt she'll find a suitable gentleman.'

'If someone did marry her solely on account of her dowry, it wouldn't speak highly of him, would it?' he asked kindly. 'Besides, you err. I know one who would marry her, dowered or not.'

'Probably someone old and fusty,' she said scornfully.

'Not so old and not so fusty.'

'Who?'

'Me.'

Amanda bounced out of her chair. 'Well, that's different. I always did think that she nursed a *tendre* for you. Wait until I tell her!'

'I think I should have that honour, don't you?' Stanwyck asked as he heard Roxanne's voice in the hall. 'She hasn't accepted me yet. Not a word, minx,' he warned.

'Amanda, here is the book. Oh, Stanwyck.' Roxanne came to a halt in front of the Marquis. 'I didn't know you were here.'

'I'm going to show Lady Haverly Byron's poetry,' Amanda said, snatching the volume from her cousin. 'Everything shall be all right. Just say yes to Stanwyck, please, Roxanne.'

She left the room like a whirlwind, and Roxanne turned puzzled eyes to the Marquis. '"Yes to Stanwyck"? What does that mean?'

He shook his head. 'That little minx. I'll wring her neck! But first, I bear a message from my heir.'

She held up a hand. 'Before you say another word, I must tell you that you were right about Jonathon and me. I've decided not to accept his offer.'

'He came to much the same conclusion. Now that that is settled, I can get on with what I want to do. Miss Franklin'—he picked up her hand and gazed intently into her eyes—'will you marry me?'

'Stanwyck, what are you doing? Stop this nonsense,' she said, pulling her hand away.

Her reaction cut him to the quick. 'Nonsense? What sort of female calls an honest offer of marriage nonsense?'

'What has Amanda told you?' she demanded. 'No doubt she's spun some Banbury tale to induce you to offer for me. It's quite unnecessary.'

'Of course it's unnecessary,' he said, sitting back on his heels. 'I never offer for a female out of necessity. And if you think one of Amanda's addled stories could induce me to offer for anyone, you are sorely mistaken.'

'Then Gwen must have said something. Or is it on account of the announcement about Webbe and Mrs Goodheart? I know it must be hard to bear that disappointment after duelling over her.'

'I didn't fight any duel over her,' Stanwyck said, rising from the floor.

'Yes, you did. I heard all about it. You were wounded, too, in the most dastardly way.'

'I didn't fight over Drusilla, pea-goose. It was over you.'

'Me?' She coloured, and paced agitatedly across the room. 'Now I know you're bamming me. Webbe would never duel over me. How *dare* you make me the object of such sport! This must be another of your odious wagers. What is at stake this time?'

'Nothing but my future,' he said intently, taking her by the shoulders and forcing her to look at him. 'Listen to me. I wish Webbe happy with Drusilla. I doubt he'll get it, but I wish it to him. I know it sounds odd. He said some cutting things about you at White's. Ben and I took exception to them. Ben, being younger, flung his glove at Webbe before I could. Dudley and I invented a ploy whereby I would take Ben's place. He was no match for Webbe.'

'So you fought the duel to save Ben,' she cried.

'Partly, but also because I don't like hearing the woman I love referred to with anything but the proper respect.'

Her pulse fluttered wildly in her throat. 'The woman you love?'

'Yes. You, dearest Roxanne.'

She broke from the embrace he had tried to wrap her in.

'But you don't love me, Stanwyck. Everyone in London knows that you love Drusilla.'

'I wish to God I had never heard of Dru,' he said hotly. 'It's true I was besotted with her when I was younger. But I was in love with a false image of her that I carried through the years. Dash it all, I was a mere stripling when I fell in love with her. Now I've changed. She's changed, too. She's not the woman I love any more. You are! I am offering you marriage, my dear Roxanne, not because of Amanda or Gwen or Webbe, but because the idea of marrying anyone else is unthinkable. Blast it, I love you!' He punctuated this declaration by taking her in his arms and kissing her wildly on the face and mouth. For one dizzying moment Roxanne feared she might swoon, but that would never do in the midst of anything so enjoyable. Reluctantly she broke the embrace.

'Do I take it that that is a Yes?' he asked huskily.

She gave a happy nod and buried her head in his coat, then almost at once drew away.

'What is it now?' he expostulated.

'Your arm.'

'It's fine.'

She settled back, then drew up again with a start. 'Lord Stanwyck.'

'Nigel,' he corrected.

She smiled. 'Nigel. In all conscience, I must acquaint you with a change in my circumstances. My cousin, as you know, left me ten thousand pounds, but after the expenses of the Season and several loans to Amanda, I find I have little left. I may have little dowry to bring into our marriage.' She gazed up at him soberly. 'If you wish to rethink the matter and withdraw your offer, I shall understand.'

'The only think I wish to rethink is whether to kiss you on the lips or the cheek,' he said, deciding on the former.

Fifteen minutes later, Amanda burst into the parlour.

'Roxanne, he's here, he's here!'

Roxanne looked up from her comfortable position in the Marquis's arms, her hair slightly dishevelled.

'Who's here?' she asked absently.

'Freddie Devens.'

'Oh, heavens.'

'Please, won't you meet him? I know he'd like to meet you and thank you for the money you lent him.'

'I suppose it shan't hurt,' Roxanne agreed. She glanced at Stanwyck and basked in the warmth of his gaze.

Quick as a flash, Amanda was gone and then back with a tall, rather gawky young man whom she introduced as Freddie Devens.

'Pleased to meet you,' Roxanne said, her words nearly drowned out by a muffled oath from her betrothed.

'What sort of hoax is this, Amanda?' Stanwyck demanded.

Amanda looked up, startled. 'Hoax?'

The Marquis looked from her bewildered face to the playwright.

'By Jove, the chit doesn't know, does she, McFarland?'

The other man shook his head. 'No, Stanwyck, she doesn't.'

Amanda stood like a stock. 'What are you talking about?' she demanded.

'This, Miss Franklin, is not Freddie Devens,' the Marquis said with some relish.

'Yes, it is.'

'This is Peter Meredith, otherwise known as Lord McFarland.'

'You're bosky,' Amanda hooted. 'Tell him so, Freddie.'

'Actually, Amanda, Stanwyck is right. I am McFarland.'

'You are? But why didn't you tell me?'

He looked abashed. 'I suppose because it was more romantic to be poor, struggling, Freddie. You did find him appealing.'

'I suppose I did,' she admitted. 'Is that why you fought shy of meeting people?'

'I couldn't risk the exposure until my play was performed. Now, it doesn't matter. I don't have much talent for the theatre.'

'Don't say that,' she said loyally.

He smiled fondly at her. 'Dear Amanda. I called to repay your cousin her four thousand pounds. It's safely back in your account with Mr Child,' he told Roxanne.

'Thank you,' Roxanne said, unable to think of anything else to say. Amanda's starving playwright, a peer? Would wonders never cease?

'Are you very rich, Freddie?' Amanda asked naïvely.

'Rich enough,' he replied. 'But Father has threatened to cut me off without a groat unless I reform my ways and find a suitable bride. That's where you come in.'

'Me, Freddie? I mean, Lord McFarland?'

'Try Peter,' he said as he drew her into his arms.

'Is he very rich?' Roxanne asked Stanwyck as they stole out of the room, leaving the younger couple alone.

'Very,' Stanwyck replied. 'Is it so important?'

'No, but it is more comfortable that way. Although Amanda is very young to contemplate marriage.'

'Amanda is older than either you or I. And wild horses wouldn't drag her from McFarland. I dare say an engagement of a year's time will convince McFarland's people of her innate goodness. And give you time to get used to the idea as well.'

'He seems a likeable chap.'

'The best of good fellows.'

'It was civil of him to return my four thousand pounds.'

'I only hope that it doesn't cause a change in our plans?'

Her eyes flew up to his, seeing the laughter there. 'Change? Why on earth...?'

'Now that you are once again an heiress, Jonathon might renew his courtship.'

She laughed, feeling happier than any one woman had a right to. 'Jonathon and his courtship may go to the devil,' she said recklessly, and lifted her face up for his kiss.

UNPREDICTABLE, COMPELLING AND TOTALLY READABLE

MIDNIGHT JEWELS – *Jayne Ann Krentz*   £2.95

Jayne Ann Krentz, bestselling author of *Crystal Flame*, blends romance and tension in her latest fast-moving novel. An advert for a rare collector's item sparked not only Mercy Pennington's meeting with the formidable Croft Falconer, but also a whole sequence of unpredictable events.

SOMETHING SO RIGHT – *Emilie Richards*   £2.75

The high-flying lifestyle of top recording artist Joelle Lindsay clashed with her attempts to return to her simple roots. This compelling novel of how love conquers disillusionment will captivate you to the last page.

GATHERING PLACE – *Marisa Carroll*   £2.50

Sarah Austin could not confront the future before she had settled her past trauma of having had her child adopted. Her love for Tyler Danielson helped, but she could not understand how his orphaned son seemed so uncannily familiar.

These three new titles will be out in bookshops from July 1989.

WORLDWIDE

Available from Boots, Martins, John Menzies, W. H. Smith, Woolworths and other paperback stockists.

COMING SOON FROM MILLS & BOON!

Your chance to win the fabulous

VAUXHALL ASTRA
MERIT 1.2 5-DOOR

Plus

**2000 RUNNER UP PRIZES OF WEEKEND
BREAKS & CLASSIC LOVE SONGS ON CASSETTE**

SEE
♥ MILLS & BOON BOOKS ♥
THROUGHOUT JULY & AUGUST FOR DETAILS!

**Offer available through Boots, Martins, John Menzies, WH Smith,
Woolworths and all good paperback stockists in the UK, Eire and Overseas.**

AROUND THE WORLD WORDSEARCH
COMPETITION!

How would you like a years supply of Mills & Boon Romances ABSOLUTELY FREE? Well, you can win them! All you have to do is complete the word puzzle below and send it in to us by October 31st. 1989. The first 5 correct entries picked out of the bag after that date will win **a years supply of Mills & Boon Romances** (*ten books every month - **worth around £150***) What could be easier?

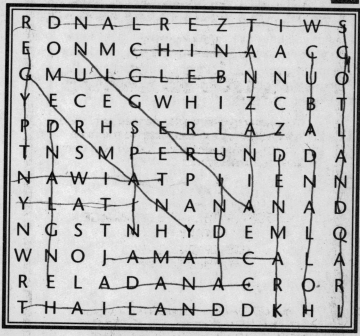

```
R D N A L R E Z T I W S
E O N M C H I N A A C C
G M U I G L E B N N U O
Y E C E G W H I Z C B T
P D R H S E R I A Z A L
T N S M P E R U N D D A
N A W I A T P I E N D N
Y L A T I N A N A N A D
N G S T N H Y D E M L Q
W N O J A M A I C A L A
R E L A D A N A C R O R
T H A I L A N D D D K H I
```

ITALY	THAILAND	SCOTLAND	SWITZERLAND
GERMANY	IRAQ	JAMAICA	
HOLLAND	ZAIRE	TANZANIA	PLEASE TURN
BELGIUM	TAIWAN	PERU	OVER FOR
EGYPT	CANADA	SPAIN	DETAILS
CHINA	INDIA	DENMARK	ON HOW
NIGERIA	ENGLAND	CUBA	TO ENTER

HOW TO ENTER

All the words listed overleaf, below the word puzzle, are hidden in the grid. You can find them by reading the letters forward, backwards, up or down, or diagonally. When you find a word, circle it or put a line through it, the remaining letters (which you can read from left to right, from the top of the puzzle through to the bottom) will spell a secret message.

After you have filled in all the words, don't forget to fill in your name and address in the space provided and pop this page in an envelope (you don't need a stamp) and post it today. Hurry - competition ends October 31st. 1989.

Mills & Boon Competition,
FREEPOST,
P.O. Box 236,
Croydon,
Surrey. CR9 9EL

Only one entry per household

Secret Message _____

_____

Name _____

Address _____

_____

_____

_____ Postcode _____

You may be mailed as a result of entering this competition

COMP 6